X Stories:
The Personal Side of fragile X syndrome

X Stories
The Personal Side
of fragile X syndrome

Edited by
Charles W. Luckmann & Paul S. Piper

Flying Trout
PRESS

Bellingham, Washington

Charles W. Luckmann teaches poetry, creative writing, literature, and ethnic studies at Skagit Valley College in Mount Vernon, Washington. Paul Piper is a librarian at Western Washington University and co-editor of *Father Nature*, published by University of Iowa Press.

Flying Trout Press
P.O. Box 1256
Bellingham, Washington 98227-1256
www.flyingtroutpress.org

Flying Trout Press is a tax-exempt charitable organization (IRS I.D.# 20-1487477) organized exclusively for charitable, educational, and literary purposes, including, for such purposes, the making of distributions to organizations that qualify as exempt organizations under Section 501(c)(3) of the Internal Revenue code, or the corresponding section of any future tax code. The mission of Flying Trout Press is to promote and publish art and literature about the disabled, especially those affected by fragile X syndrome and autism; to promote and publish art and literature about the natural and cultural landscapes of the American West; and to promote and publish art and literature by first-time authors.

The publication of this book was generously supported by grants from The Lucky Seven Foundation of Seattle and by individual donations.

Printed in the United States of America

ISBN: 0-9785203-0-0
This book was designed by James Walters.
The cover illustration is *Self Portrait* by Noah Douglas Luckmann.
The manuscript was copyedited by Cheryll Greenwood Kinsley.

This book is printed on acid-free paper.

For Noah Douglas Luckmann

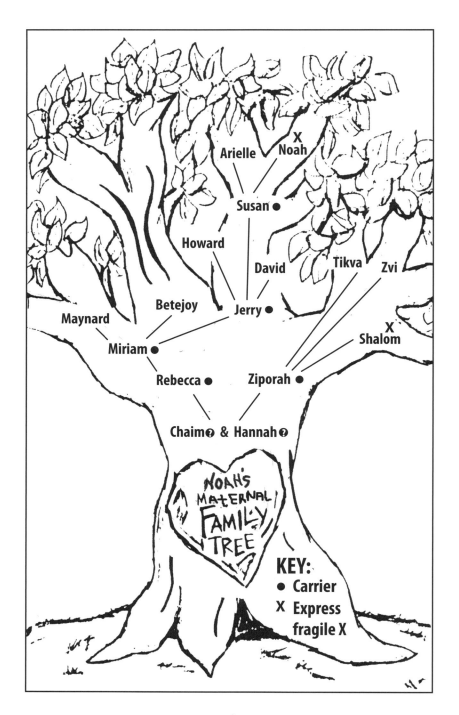

Some Facts About Fragile X

One afternoon in 1991 when my son Noah was 18 months old, a few weeks after scientists discovered the FMR1 gene that causes fragile X syndrome, I took Noah from our home in Seattle across the floating bridge spanning Lake Washington to Bellevue, to see a neurologist our pediatrician said was one of the best in Washington State.

A few weeks later my wife and I got the diagnosis that Noah had fragile X. That day we started a journey of confusion, learning, and change that is still unfolding, for my family and for tens of thousands of other families who have received similar diagnoses. According to the National Fragile X Foundation and the Fragile X Research Foundation (FRAXA), fragile X syndrome—a genetic disorder—is the world's leading cause of inherited mental impairment. It is also the cause of a condition in some adult carriers that resembles Parkinson's disease and is known as FXTAS: fragile X-associated tremor ataxia syndrome.

Fragile X syndrome is caused by a specific mutation of the FMR1 gene that is located on the long arm of the X chromosome. People who have fragile X may exhibit a variety of symptoms that can be mistaken for other conditions. Although fragile X and FXTAS can be accurately identified with a simple DNA test, many people who carry fragile X mutations are either undiagnosed or misdiagnosed. Individuals with a *premutation*—a small defect in the gene—show no symptoms but are carriers and can pass fragile X to their children. Many people do not realize they are carriers. According to the Centers for Disease Control as reported by FRAXA, "fragile X affects 1 in 4000 males and 1 in 6000 females of all races and ethnic groups. About 1 in 259 women carry fragile X and could pass it to their children. About 1 in 800 men carry fragile X; their daughters will also be carriers."

This genetic volatility is passed from generation to generation, often moving silently to affect individuals like Noah with a full mutation of the defective FMR1 gene. A full mutation switches off the production of proteins needed for typical neural development. At this time there is no cure for fragile X.

If you suspect someone you know might have fragile X syndrome or be a carrier, or if you simply want more information about this all too common but still mysterious and often misunderstood disease, we're glad you found this book. We've included a list of organizations and sources of additional information, but what you'll find in *X Stories* that makes our book unique are personal essays written by people whose lives have been profoundly affected by fragile X syndrome.

Much of what has been written about fragile X is technical. But *X Stories* presents in their own words how fragile X has transformed people's lives. It begins with stories about family life just before and right after diagnosis. The stories continue across generations, as fragile X carriers and fully affected individuals move into adolescence, adulthood, and old age. But this book is not just for parents or families who share an inherited genetic syndrome or similar "disability." It's for everyone who has ever faced challenges and coped with life's unexpected, disruptive events—and learned how to grow into the people we were meant to become.

Contents

Siblings

Preface

This book is rooted in very personal soil.

We were introduced to each other by a mutual friend several years ago and soon found we had much in common. We're both from Illinois. We're around the same age. Both of us are writers and academics with an interest in outdoor sports and activities. And we each have family members who are mentally impaired. Chuck's son, Noah, has fragile X syndrome and Paul's brother Todd is autistic.

As our families socialized, we discussed our shared interests and experiences. Primary among them was how the experience of having a son or a sibling with an illness such as fragile X or autism affects one's life. Somewhere along the line we got the idea to start a nonprofit literary press. We discussed different emphases, but the idea that kept surfacing—and the one that seemed significantly underrepresented— was to advance the literature of disabilities, particularly autism and fragile X syndrome.

After Flying Trout Press received its federal 501(c)(3) status as a charitable organization, we began mapping out what our first book might look like. We were both intrigued by personal stories and by the autobiographical literary form called the personal essay. These essays vary in composition, but they often employ metaphor, narrative juxtaposition, allusion, and other literary devices while retaining a core of personal observation and emotional response. We decided that was the direction for us. We would focus on collecting personal essays about fragile X.

The book that emerged, the book you now hold in your hands, deviates a bit from our early plans and projections. To create a work that can be judged solely on its literary merit requires literary work from professional writers. As we advertised for and began receiving submissions, we realized that many people profoundly affected by fragile X—whether as a carrier, parent, sibling, or caregiver—were not professional writers, but witnesses. They live with fragile X every day.

We were so moved by these stories that we honed in on this area of witness. Chuck secured a four-month sabbatical, which allowed him time to help many of the essayists with the technical aspects of telling their stories. In these pages you will also find professional writers, as well as scientists and researchers. Their words help to unravel some of the mysteries of the fragile X disease. But the triumph of this book, for us, is that it gives voice to the people who by a quirk of genetics have been thrown into lives that can only be survived by humor, heroism, and often deep spirituality. Theirs are the predominate voices you will hear as you read.

If you enjoy the stories in our book, we hope to hear from you. And if you have your own experiences with fragile X, we hope you'll share them with us.

Charles W. Luckmann & Paul S. Piper
Bellingham, Washington
May 2006

Introduction

Mary Jane Clark is a best-selling novelist and a producer at CBS News. Her son David has fragile X syndrome.

Each spring, when the forsythia blooms bright yellow, I am reminded of the days right after we got the diagnosis. David, our second child, the 7-month-old baby who'd earned a perfect 10 Apgar score in the delivery room, had something called fragile X syndrome. I'd never heard of it, never knew it existed, never imagined I could be carrying it in my gene pool.

Sunshine streamed in through the hospital window as David's father and I listened to a doctor and genetic counselor lay out the facts. Fragile X is the most common form of genetically transferred mental impairment, which can range from mild learning disabilities to mental retardation. Boys are more often and more severely affected than girls. Other symptoms can include language delays, extreme hyperactivity, anxiety, obsessive-compulsive disorders, and autistic-like behaviors. As the medical professionals explained that it was transferred on the X chromosome, it dawned on me that David's then 5-year-old sister could be a carrier as well. And perhaps the most eye-opening of all were the possible scenarios painted for David's future, none of them very hopeful.

When the meeting was over and we went outside, the birds still chirped and the crisp spring breeze still blew, but our world had totally changed. I walked to the car in a daze as I tried to make sense of the staggering information. There had been no mental retardation that I knew of in my family, yet I was a carrier. If fragile X was the most common form of genetically transferred mental impairment, why had I never heard or read anything about it? What kind of life would David have and who would take care of him when his parents were gone? Was I going to be able to do a good job in raising a child with special needs?

I felt completely unprepared and overwhelmed at the thought of what lay ahead. Oh, how I wish there had been a book then like *X Stories: The Personal Side of fragile X syndrome*. But how glad I am that 17 years later, there is one now.

The book you hold in your hands is appropriately named. The personal stories shared in these pages convey a wide range of powerful emotions and impart a joint wisdom. There are examples of great strength and deep despair. There are stories of hope and joy, while others will bring tears to your eyes or take your breath away. There is an unflinching honesty that can only, in the end, be a good thing because it provides knowledge and perspective. In reading the stories that are presented here, we all can benefit from the expertise and varying points of view of mothers, fathers, siblings, caregivers, and professionals who have experienced fragile X syndrome up close and personal.

Tales of fears, frustrations, heartbreak, acceptance, trials, and triumphs are all represented here. A handbook for all of us who live with the consequences of fragile X, *X Stories: The Personal Side of fragile X syndrome*, is a companion to reassure us that we are not alone.

Mary Jane Clark
April 2006

Acknowledgments

X Stories would not have been possible without generous financial support from The Lucky Seven Foundation of Seattle, Washington. We thank them for their faith in us and for seeing merit in this project.

We would like to thank the following people for their donations to Flying Trout Press. Their trust in us means a great deal and their financial support is invaluable:

Associates in Family Medicine, Robert H. & Barbara Schmidt, Kelly McAvoy, Russell Graham, Jim Bertolino, Robert & Deidre Kent, Linda & Rick McPhee, Tim Pilgrim, Joan Beardsley, Susan Rachel Specter, Eric A. Yaremko, Michael Lippitz and Susan Wagner, Carl Griesser, Syrall & Bud Specter, Nancy and Bill Brewer, Ellie & Robert Slabodnick, Peter & Linda Chorney, Sandy Farringer, Miguel & Heidi Ramos, David & Maggie Carlson, Jill & Bob Musselman, Jo & Art Baner, Karin & Bob Gellatly, Cynthia & Sydney Wexler, Nancy & Curt Glass, Rick Osen, Mary Beth Dietrick, Roger & Holly Sharf, Kelly & Jason Graham, Baz Stevens, Patrick Feeney, Will Hornyak, Stan & Sylvia Tag, Doug Lewis, Ben & Kim Henwood, Sue & Gary Peltz, Ray & Margaret Carlson, Bill Fitzhugh, Robert Vanderpoel, David Taylor, Charles Piper, William & June Luckmann, Betejoy & Arthur Oleisky, Stephen Loring, John & Becky Luckmann, Penny & John Snyder, Robert & Priscilla Phillips, Lillian & George Perkins, Mary Lubben & Ed Zotti, William Eleson, Thomas Stone, and Elizabeth C. Harris.

Several organizations helped us locate authors. These include the Fragile X Association of Washington State, the Fragile X Association of Georgia, the Fragile X Association of Australia, FRAXA Research Foundation, and the National Fragile X Foundation (NFXF). When we started this project, Katie Clapp, executive director of FRAXA, and Robert Miller, executive editor of NFXF, were especially helpful in getting the word out. Katie Clapp, Mary Jane Clark, and John Harrigan read the early drafts of this book. Their encouraging comments helped move it closer to production.

We are also indebted to Skagit Valley College. They gave Chuck four months to work with the authors during the critical months of revising and editing rough drafts. And we thank *Men's Journal* and Paul Solotaroff for permission to reprint "X-Man And Me."

We also want to acknowledge the help of Timothy Pilgrim, one of our board members and professor of journalism at Western Washington University, who read and edited the first complete draft.

Cheryll Greenwood Kinsley, owner of CGK Wordsmith, was our copyeditor. She helped turn our indecision into decisions and tie up loose ends. James Walters, graphic artist and layout designer, was also indispensable. Like Cheryll, he was constantly cheerful. We thank them both.

It is not as an afterthought that we thank Susie Specter and Joan Piper, our marriage partners. Without their support, this book—and so much else—would be impossible. We are deeply grateful to them and we thank them for sharing our lives.

Artist: Ben Loeliger

Ben Loeliger, a junior in high school, is an honors student who plans to become an architect or engineer. He is a fragile X carrier and has a 12-year-old brother, Austin, with the full fragile X mutation.

In this picture I used a lot of symbolism. I represented each member of my family with a hidden letter. My brother, Darrin, and my Dad are represented by two arches that look like the letter "D." I am represented by my signature. My mother is represented by an "M" formed by the stalactites hanging from the top right island. My brother Kevin is represented by a crack shaped like a "K" on the lower right island; and of course Austin, who likes to swing, is represented by the swing set inside the lower left island. The whole picture is shaped like the fragile X with the broken staircase and ladder to represent the weak spots and the word "Fragile" appears twice in the top right tree.

Beginnings

Our Son Is Different:
Our Journey To His Diagnosis

Heather Vinduska is the mother of a son with fragile X syndrome.

Had I known what the message was on the answering machine,
I would never have let my mom leave my house that day. We had just
come from the park. I saw the light blinking but wanted to tell my mom
good-bye and get her on the road to her home before I tended to my
personal business. I had no idea I was going to hear life-changing news.
I didn't know I was about to find out just what made my son Vincent
so different from other kids. What I found on the answering machine
wasn't news I wanted to hear alone.

It took almost four years and the birth of a second child before my
husband and I started looking for answers.

After a textbook pregnancy and three uneventful attempts to induce
labor, our son Vincent had been born by C-section late on a Tuesday
afternoon. I was quite groggy, but I remember asking with some sort
of coherency if he had all his fingers and toes, if he was normal. When
they told me all "the parts were there," I was filled with such a feeling

of relief. In one of my graduate courses I remembered discussing prenatal development and all the disabilities that can occur. I felt like I had made it over the hump. Now I had this beautiful child. His physical appearance was angelically perfect. After being so careful during my pregnancy, we had succeeded. Everything about him looked and seemed completely normal. What I didn't know was that the years to follow would be an emotional roller coaster. My initial feeling of relief would gradually wear away.

As an infant, Vincent was a wonderful baby. He smiled easily and was good tempered 99 percent of the time. He was healthy and had no ear infections, only minor colds and mild flu. When he was 9 weeks old, I returned to work. On the evening of my first day back, he began to allow me full nights of sleep.

But our concerns about Vincent started early. Friends of ours who had a child similar in age to Vincent would be amazed at how their infant, even at a few days of age, would watch them and imitate simple facial movements or visually track an object. We didn't get those kinds of responses from Vincent. He just didn't seem that attentive to us. As the months rolled on we began noticing other children his age in daycare were progressing faster in their development. They were already rolling over, sitting up, crawling, and pulling up to stand. Vincent still seemed like such a young baby. Our babysitter told us not to compare him to other children because they all grow up differently. This was our first child, our first attempt at parenting this offspring of ours who unfortunately had arrived without an instruction manual. We had no idea what to expect.

I wasn't religious about charting Vincent's developmental milestones, but I do remember he was 11 months of age when he first began crawling. About a month after learning to crawl, he began pulling up to stand. He would then easily walk around furniture but never ventured to take steps on his own. It was as if he didn't know what came next. Our pediatrician was on my case constantly to take him off the bottle by his first birthday. I took his comments under advisement but my gut feeling was that Vincent wasn't ready to give up the bottle.

He just wasn't drinking easily enough from a cup. Also, at about a year of age, he started waking up crying every night at least one time, usually more often. The only way to comfort him and get him back to sleep was to give him a bottle. Eventually the only time he was given a bottle was during the night. This behavior continued until Vincent was 2 1/2, when he began sleeping through the night again. This ended his need for the bottle. He finally started walking unassisted just a week shy of 19 months. I reasoned that walking at this age was not extremely delayed, but at the same time I knew it was not exactly typical.

We continued to have some concern about Vincent's development but the milestones did come, just later than usual. I decided he was on the slower end and would eventually catch up. One thing that did ease my mind about Vincent was his love for books. Even in his early months of life, he would attend very closely to a book. By 9 months of age he would imitate us reading to him. He would open the book and begin babbling "gibberish." He would turn each page, smack his lips, and continue his "reading." It was really comical. There were many occasions when I was sure this high-level imitation, as I called it, indicated that he was progressing just fine.

As we had just moved, Vincent was seen by a new pediatrician for his well-check at 18 months. This doctor had not yet seen Vincent's other medical records or reviewed his history. We voiced our concern about Vincent's apparently slow development. He wasn't really using words at this point and he wasn't walking on his own. The doctor asked a few questions and administered a short developmental screening, which indicated Vincent showed delays in all areas. She questioned whether his hearing was normal and inquired about past ear infections. Vincent had been free and clear of any ear infections up to this point. I knew from my own observations (and my past audiology courses as a graduate student) that he could hear normally. She insisted that we test Vincent's hearing status anyway, which angered me because she didn't consider us to be experts on our own child. She then mentioned that with these delays in development and his hand flapping—which we had never thought anything of—he might have fragile X syndrome.

I immediately thought this doctor was jumping to conclusions way too quickly. A professional cannot diagnose anything from a screening test. From my training in college I knew a screening merely indicates whether further testing is warranted.

The doctor went on to say this syndrome is known to be more prominent in males and has characteristics such as mild to moderate mental retardation, hand flapping, and developmental delays. Now she was indicating he was mentally retarded! How dare she say such a thing! In addition to this, she suggested that we take him for further testing and seek genetic counseling before having more children.

I was appalled. First this doctor casually throws a diagnosis at us after spending 15 minutes with Vincent. Then she indicates that he might be mentally retarded and tacks on the issue of genetic counseling? Vincent wasn't a monster. He was a sweet, happy child who laughed and smiled and loved easily. The words "mental retardation" literally made us go numb. We came in for a well-check with a few developmental concerns and left feeling completely shocked, angry, and in total disbelief. This doctor had no right to even mention a condition such as this to us after a mere screening test! It was way too early in the game to be giving us the worst-case scenario. We never returned to this doctor and foolishly decided not to act on her recommendations.

The summer following this spring appointment, I was fortunate enough to have my younger sister be our nanny for Vincent. She stayed with us until she returned to college in the fall and spent a lot of one-on-one time with him. In fact, she was the one who witnessed the first true word from Vincent: "truck." It was not your typical first word. He said it as he watched a truck drive past the park that day. We had decided we were going to wait until summer ended before making a decision about proceeding with developmental testing.

Any visits to the swimming pool that summer with Vincent left the parent more tired than the child. Vincent was almost uncontrollable in the water. He splashed and flailed his arms constantly and squealed with excitement. It was as if he just couldn't contain himself. As I was trying to keep him from wiggling out of my arms, I noticed another child that looked to be about his same age. She was holding onto her mother and calmly interacting, learning to blow bubbles in the water and kicking her feet. I just couldn't get Vincent to calm down enough to attend to me like this. There was something about him that set him apart from other kids, but I couldn't quite put my finger on it. It was a maternal instinct that something just wasn't right. When he was in day care and I came to pick him up, he would walk through the room, maybe look at me, and just keep walking by. He never ran up to me like he was happy I was there. I always saw the other children do that.

As summer came to an end, we still had concerns the more we observed other children Vincent's age. At 21 months Vincent still didn't communicate with us using meaningful words. He didn't call us "mama" or "dada," although he could point to us in a picture when asked. He was more active than other children. He wouldn't sit still very long to do any activity. He had begun hand biting when excited and developed a large callous on his left hand. He laughed and smiled easily and with that he seemed to be a very social child, but he didn't play with other children and interact. Instead, he played right next to them. He didn't fall asleep easily at nap time or at night. He was a very skinny child who ate enormous portions of food.

As I look back, I don't know if it was pride or the urge to keep Vincent's problems quiet in our small town of 2,100 people. I didn't want his grade-school teachers to know that he was slow as a young child. I thought they would have lower expectations of him if they knew about his early years. I wanted to get him "caught up" before entering school; then no one except us would know his history. I made some calls to the nearest large city—about 60 miles away—and inquired about getting a full developmental evaluation. I found this couldn't be done as we were outside that county. So I made a phone call to the early childhood cooperative in our county and scheduled an evaluation for Vincent.

Early intervention services for children Vincent's age were provided in our home by early childhood development professionals. They were wonderful, caring people. Debbi, the early education teacher, first assessed all areas of Vincent's development. Her evaluation indicated at 22 months of age Vincent demonstrated developmental skills (fine motor, gross motor, social skills) at the 16- to 19-month range. He wasn't profoundly delayed; but it was enough to qualify him for early intervention services. She then recommended further evaluation by a speech therapist. She had concerns about language delays, as did I. Debbi's testing indicated Vincent's language skills were at the 3- to 6-month-old level.

It was here that I felt a bit inadequate as Vincent's mother. I was a speech therapist myself. I had been working with Vincent, trying to stimulate his language since the day he was born. I must admit that child language was not my forte, as my area of employment had always been with adults, by choice. That was what interested me the most. Fresh out of school I was employed at a rehabilitation hospital as a member of a stroke team. I then went on to work in long-term care facilities. I suppose I should have focused more on child language in college. Of course, hindsight is 20/20! Due to my focus in my profession, I didn't own any tests for child language.

I found out as our life unraveled that there were so many things I was blind to—and biased about—when observing my own child. With all this considered, however, my background still proved to be a luxury not all parents have. I was at least able to identify that Vincent was not developing at a typical rate and that he was exhibiting delays in his language. Moreover, I was better able to understand the results of Vincent's test scores. All this knowledge is good, but there were times I wished I didn't know quite so much.

Fortunately, a few months after we began early intervention services, I was able to resign from my job and stay home to concentrate on Vincent and give him more one-on-one time. With early intervention services and more attention at home, we started seeing some progress. Vincent was receiving a weekly visit from both the early childhood teacher and the speech therapist. Despite his progress, I still knew something was different about him every time I noticed the behaviors of other children his age. With Vincent, there just didn't seem to be that parent-child connection. He didn't attend to or respond to us like other children did to their parents. It's not that I felt he was autistic. There was just something odd or different that I couldn't identify.

Ignoring the genetic counseling recommendation, we endured two miscarriages before our daughter, Grace, entered our lives. Vincent was 3 1/2 years old at this time. We were not really sure how he would take this new presence in our home. Although we told Vincent that he was going to have a little sister, I'm not sure the information really registered. When he entered our hospital room to see Grace, it was as if in his own little way he knew this baby was special to him. It was the sweetest thing to witness. He went right up to her and kissed her on the forehead. I will never forget that moment. He then proceeded to climb up beside me and began to point at my IV and whimper like it upset him. He really must have had some kind of understanding of the situation. When we brought Grace home, Vincent was the sweetest, most gentle big brother he could be. I could tell he loved her in his own "special" way.

Grace brought us her own set of worries. One nostril was slightly smaller than the other, which in reality was not of great concern. However, she also had a small physical abnormality by her right ear, what they called a skin tag. I had heard of these while in college. The presence of a skin tag by an ear can indicate kidney malformation and/or hearing loss. A sonogram indicated the kidneys were fine. A hearing screening was administered when she was only a few hours old, conducted by the hospital's audiologist. Grace didn't pass the hearing screening in the right ear. Four weeks later during a follow-up screening, it was indicated that her hearing was worse in the right ear than it had been just after birth. I distinctly remember the first few words of the audiologist, "It's just a birth defect. She will still be considered a hearing child with her normal ear. There are so many advances in research...." She lost me as shock set in.

This audiologist did not refer us on for a medical evaluation, so under my own recommendation we made an emergency appointment with an ear, nose, and throat specialist. I was just sick with fear that something was terribly wrong with a 4-week-old infant whose hearing had deteriorated since birth. I had all sorts of scenarios going through my mind. I worried it might be a tumor on one of her cranial nerves or something else just as serious. The ENT doctor examined Grace and concluded that her right ear canal was much more narrow than the left. Therefore it probably caused an error in testing and, thus, false test results. He recommended giving her some time to grow and screening her again in three to four months. I was quite relieved but still very worried. Life was throwing us another curve. We had Vincent, who was a puzzle to us, and now Grace, who might be partially deaf.

With everything up to this point taken into account—Vincent's delayed development, Grace's questionable hearing status, our two miscarriages, and the fact that my sister's son and daughter were also experiencing developmental delays—we began to ponder the idea that maybe there was indeed something genetic involved here. We started to wonder if there was some undiagnosed disability in our family.

At Grace's next well-check with our family doctor, we relayed our reasons for concern. The doctor concluded that genetic testing was warranted.

A few short weeks later we took both children to a pediatrician who specialized in genetics. At this time Grace was 3 months old and Vincent was almost 4 years. We gave an extensive family history to the best of our knowledge. The doctor then began a physical assessment on Grace, noting her eye contact, how attentive she was, the height of the roof of her mouth, and so forth. He asked us various questions about the pregnancy and her development since birth. While this was going on, Vincent was a very busy boy in this tiny examination room. He was in constant motion. He was touching, shaking, moving, adjusting, rubbing, brushing against, pounding on, licking—yes, licking!—and opening everything within his reach. When the doctor finished his assessment on Grace, he concluded that he didn't see any reason to test her at this point. However, without even asking us one question about Vincent, he turned to him and stated, "But I do want to test him." I think Vincent was showing his true colors that day. Nothing needed to be asked or said about him. It was plainly obvious that Vincent had some issues.

That day the doctor diagnosed Vincent with Attention Deficit Hyperactive Disorder (ADHD). This came as no surprise to us. We then obtained a blood and urine sample from Vincent, a process I wish to keep repressed in my memory as something others need not imagine. The samples were then sent off to the appropriate labs. We were told the results would be back in approximately four weeks. Vincent was being tested for many things, both genetic and metabolic.

Those weeks of waiting were somewhat of a blur. My thoughts bounced on an hourly basis between being either worried sick or confident there could be nothing wrong with my child. It could just be the ADHD holding things up. Everything in my life up to this point had been, by anyone's standards, normal. That's just the way it was. Then, after only three weeks of waiting, there was this blinking light on the answering machine signaling a message that would radically alter my life.

I waved good-bye to my mom as she left for her two-hour drive home. I rounded up the kids and took them inside so I could check the phone message. Having no idea it was the genetics pediatrician himself calling, I pressed the button. In his message he identified himself and said he had a diagnosis on Vincent. He then proceeded to say that he would see us at our scheduled appointment next week or I could call him back today if I wanted. I went numb at the words "diagnosis on Vincent." They had indeed identified something, which did not sound promising. There was no way I was going to wait a week. The results were in and I wanted them that day. My gut told me that this would not be good, so I wanted to hear the news in the privacy of my home.

My husband was still at work but it was almost 5 p.m. I was afraid no one would be in the doctor's office this late. My heart pounded as my shaky fingers fumbled to find paper and pencil to write down the phone number. I was relieved to hear a real live person answer my call. I was passed around to several people as I explained my situation to each. I finally had to resort to having the doctor paged. He called back shortly and stated, "Vincent has fragile X." My response, which more or less reflexively rolled out, was, "How severe?" He responded that he didn't have the lab results in front of him so we would discuss it at our scheduled appointment next week. He went on to present me with more information, or what sounded somewhat like counseling to the best of my memory, but I drifted off and don't recall anything specific he said beyond that.

When I hung up the phone, I just sat there for some time, unable to move or react. Then the tears started. It only takes a good sentimental greeting card to cause my eyes to tear up, so something like this was overwhelming. Because of my educational background, the news was initially worse for me. I didn't have that usual reaction: "Well, what the heck is fragile X?" Although I didn't remember specific details, I knew immediately that this was something that would not go away, something he would not grow out of. I knew right away this was permanent. Then my mind began spinning. In my graduate program I had a course on how to counsel parents of special needs children. I knew what to "tell" myself. In this one phone call with just one sentence, it was now confirmed that I had just become one of those parents. I was now on the "other side of the fence." It is so true that there is an overwhelming feeling of loss, loss for that normal child you thought you had. I'm not a pessimist, just a realist. All the things I envisioned him doing in his life vanished and his future accomplishments became completely uncertain. I didn't know if I was crying for my own "loss" or for Vincent because of the obstacles I now knew he would have to face in his life. He would have challenges beyond what "normal" kids had. Now I could really use an instruction manual. What should I do to "be" Vincent's mother now? I just scooped him up and held him tight and cried for both of us.

Everything at that moment had changed, yet nothing was immediately different. The only difference was that we knew something we hadn't known the day before, the years before, any time before the emotional roller coaster began. I knew now it was one we would never climb off of. Now our path forward would be different. Our plans would be different.

We've now discovered that "different" does not always mean "bad." However heartbreaking this news about Vincent was, it was really a turning point for us and a positive thing for him. It was traumatic to find out that his disabilities were permanent. On the other hand, I saw my sister-in-law struggling because at that point there had been no diagnosis, no explanation for her daughter's problems, despite extensive genetic and medical testing. I used to think that maybe never knowing keeps the hope alive that the child will someday mature and grow out of their disability. But for us, getting that diagnosis was a means for us to help Vincent in the best way possible. We now knew what we were dealing with.

With that positive in mind, I decided this was not something to be down and depressed about. I loved my son, and allowing myself to drown in my own self-pity would not do a thing to help Vincent. He needed all I could give him. I started to flash back to the movie *Forrest Gump* and remembered what his mother did for him. I decided I was up for the challenge.

After Vincent was diagnosed we were able to take him to various professionals who specialized in children with fragile X. These people offered suggestions for dealing with, or decreasing, some of Vincent's symptoms and behaviors. We found out Vincent had autistic characteristics, especially in his speech patterns. He was echolalic, meaning he echoed utterances others spoke instead of forming his own novel sentences or phrases. I knew what echolalic speech was, but again, I just didn't recognize it in my own child. He would spend hours lining up objects perfectly or self-stimulating through verbal noises he made while manipulating an object of high interest to him. We also found out Vincent has sensory integration issues and craves more sensory input than most children, which explains the hand biting.

We also explored the option of medication for Vincent's ADHD. The pediatrician who diagnosed Vincent told us medication would not work for him because his ADHD was genetic-based. I guarantee if this doctor had his own child with ADHD he would think differently. We obtained a second opinion and were able to start Vincent on the stimulant Adderall. Lo and behold, the medication was effective. I can't even describe how much more manageable life is now on a daily basis, not to mention how much learning has taken place. We were able to do so much more for Vincent once we knew, and more fully understood, what made him different.

Through all this we finally attended genetic counseling. We knew it was now warranted. We wanted to know how any future children would be affected by fragile X syndrome. The revelation was not something we wanted to hear. We learned we have a fifty-fifty chance that any future child will be affected by fragile X. We had always wanted a large family. Now we are not sure.

A few months after Vincent's diagnosis, we found out Grace's hearing was normal in both ears. We have not tested her for fragile X. Developmental testing revealed she was progressing fairly normally despite a mild language delay. Vincent started kindergarten with the aid of a one-on-one paraprofessional. He is performing the best we could have expected. My sister's son and daughter have now both been diagnosed with fragile X. The emotional roller coaster has picked up speed as we are unexpectedly pregnant with our third child. The path ahead again becomes uncertain.

X-Man And Me

Paul Solotaroff, a freelance writer living in New York, is the author of **The House of Purple Hearts.** *This essay first appeared in the November 2003 issue of* **Men's Journal** *and is used here by permission.*

I was down in a catacomb keep of dreams when the sound of laughter rang through. It woke me by inches—this was the third night running—and sat me up, drunk with rage. The bedside clock said 3:47; it took all my manly rectitude not to scream.

I trudged upstairs, roundly plunking my skull on the tread of our spiral steps. Waiting for the pain to clear, I could hear my son cackling down the hall, drumming his heels in bed. Three months ago it was terror that roused him: a series of nightmares that brought him half around, moaning in fugue-state dread. Now it was hilarity, a joke he couldn't tell me, stand-up from the beyond. As a rule, of course, laughter is better than tears, but at this hour of the morning they're indivisible.

When I opened Luke's door I found him upright, a blanket swaddling his head. In the moonlight he looked like bin Laden as a toddler at terrorist camp. He yanked down the blanket, and there was that grin, as though the funniest thing imaginable would have been to waste the night sleeping when we could be up watching Elmo and eating cashews. (Having just discovered nuts, he did a hard-target search for them whenever we were in the aisles of Key Food.) It is useless to describe the effect his smile had on me—picture a man melting like processed cheese—but suffice it to say that I was under its spell. I climbed into bed and curled up with him.

Now that he had me where he wanted me, my 4-year-old trash-talked in earnest. As he knew no words beyond the handful of grunts we'd come to interpret as directives—"maaw" for I'm hungry or I want, "buh" for his favorite book of the moment (which had to be read to him 20 times per sitting), and "ahh" for the $12 remote-control cop car that he could watch go in circles for hours and that I would have risked jail time to smash—what came out of him now was a torrent of triphthongs that only the Taco Bell chihuahua could interpret. "Shhhh," I murmured, though to no known end—nothing short of a ball gag could have muted him now. Besides, how in conscience do you silence a child who is so preternaturally happy?

Still, like a madman I harbored hope of an hour or two of fitful sleep. (My wife was teaching a three-day class in Texas; otherwise it would have been her turn to shush him.) I sorted through the list of calming techniques we'd learned from Luke's therapists and teachers. Skin brushing was out, as was joint compression—those methods rarely slowed him down even during daylight hours. When he was this far gone on a nocturnal slammer of hilarity and norepinephrine, only one thing worked for us, and that only rarely. Turning him sideways, I bundled my child in a straitjacket of a hug, arms crossed firmly at his chest. He giggled and writhed—this was both heaven and hell for a boy so sensorily swamped—then ever so slowly unwound. He fought for every inch, chafing against me, chirping his birdsong dissent. Because he weighed next to nothing and had no muscle to speak of, it didn't take much to subdue him. Still, I could feel the juice coursing through him, uploads of neural current. A doctor once likened Luke's brain wiring to "a jack with 10 phones plugged in." As I lay there listening to his nonsense chat, I tried to picture life as a crowded circuit, the world pouring in unfiltered. After a beat, though, I stopped—that way lay madness, a blood-boiling rage against the gods.

At last he fell quiet, his breathing metered, his bony shoulders softened in repose. With the stealth of a burglar, I drew back my arms, sliding out from under him inch by inch. It was treacherous going—he's the lightest of sleepers—and as I eased away from him, I battled the urge to pelt his neck with kisses. A friend once told me that having a child opens parts of your heart you've never used, but this was something else again. It was wild and primitive, a caveman's love. I would have thrown myself at tigers for this boy.

I had just set my second foot on the floor when he rolled over, grinning in spades. Like a shot he was past me and out the door, to make for the secret place in the pantry where we hid the cashews.

Every expectant father, whether he admits it or not, carries around a secret book of fears. Shelved in the unconscious within easy reach at certain sleepless hours of the night, it contains a folio of what-if terrors regarding his unborn child. A botched delivery, an unseen tumor, the innocuous fever that blooms into a stroke—each of these opens into nightmare time, a child so crippled or badly maimed that life for all concerned becomes perdition. If a man indulges these kinds of thoughts—that is to say, if he's anything at all like me—he may find himself, in the run-up to his baby's arrival, engaged in some morbid bargaining. Addressing his nerves, or the god of his choice, he may say, "I can handle disfigurement or a kid with Down syndrome, but please, not paraplegia." Or, "We'll get through paralysis—there's a cure in the works—but I beg you, no lymphoma." Beyond the unthinkable—the death of an infant—his worst fears tend toward the penny-dreadful: the condition that denies the child a future and renders him a lifelong ward.

But what happens when the next-worst thing occurs, when an otherwise healthy son fails to thrive? How do you hold yourself together when your beautiful, sweet-tempered little boy goes backward as others go forward, trapped in mud and sinking further with every passing month? How do you keep your marriage going in the face of slow-burn loss, grief that seems to replenish daily and grow ever deeper? And how do you competently father a child whose needs outstrip your power to even grasp them?

My son was born, in October 1998, with a single-gene mutation called fragile X. Though virtually unknown to the general public, fragile X syndrome is the most common inherited cause of mental retardation, affecting, by some estimates, 100,000 Americans and 2 million people worldwide. It disproportionately afflicts boys—roughly one in 2,000, as opposed to one in 4,000 girls—disrupting neural connections in the brain at some point before birth. More than 80 percent of males with the fragile X defect suffer mild to severe retardation. The number in fragile X girls is only 33 percent, though the female sex has other burdens to bear: One in every 250 women in the world is a carrier of fragile X—without even knowing it, in most cases, until she gives birth to a defective child.

As it's currently incurable and of little or no interest to the drug makers that fund most research, fragile X would be catastrophic even if the cellular insult stopped there. But beyond its damage to learning and memory, the defective gene wreaks a host of behavioral woes that blight a child's chance for an engaged life. These often—but not always—include panic, depression, hypomania, attention deficit disorder, sleep disturbance, shyness, impulsivity, generalized anxiety, and hyperactivity, as well as extreme sensitivity to common stimuli such as noise, light, and touch. Additionally, kids with the fragile X mutation are much more likely to develop features of autism than are their healthy peers and are at extremely high risk for seizure disorder, which can kill them if it is not treated with powerful medication. Fragile X is, in other words, the perfect storm of genetic sabotage. It seems to blunt a child's brain, then superheats his nerves to make him an inmate in his own skin. And for crushing parents' hopes and wrecking homes, its power is hard to conjure. Well-meaning friends tell me all the time: I can just imagine your pain. No, you can't, I think but don't say. You have no idea.

18

The science of fragile X is prohibitively dense, but there are some baseline facts. Boys, to reprise a bit of freshman biology, take an X chromosome at conception from their mother and a Y from their father; girls take an X from both. Unlike many genetic diseases, the mutation that triggers fragile X starts as a mere molecular instability that lurks silently in families for generations before erupting into full disorder. The weak spot is found near one end of the X chromosome, and it can be transmitted by mothers to children of either sex or (in its latent form) by fathers to their daughters. Girls who inherit the defective gene, however, have a second, presumably healthy X, which may compensate, so even if they have the worst kind of mutation they often show no symptoms at all. Boys, of course, don't have a second X to fall back on and are far more prone to the syndrome's full effects. These include, besides the problems listed above, a set of telltale physical markers: long, oval faces with lantern jaws and large, protruding ears, loose joints and muscles and a flat-footed gait, and, at puberty, the emergence of oversize testicles.

Of the 30,000 genes in human biology, more than half are a thorough mystery to science, performing functions that can only be guessed at. But since it was isolated 12 years ago by clinicians in Australia, France, and the United States, the gene that causes fragile X has begun to yield some secrets. "We know that a defect turns the gene off before it can do its job, which is to make a crucial protein in the brain," says Dr. W. Ted Brown, chairman of human genetics at the Institute for Basic Research (IBR) on Staten Island in New York City, the first and foremost fragile X clinic in the world. "We think that protein modifies other genes that, collectively, act as editors. Without it—and the ability to tune out stimuli—a child's brain is under constant bombardment, in a more or less standing state of sensory meltdown."

One particular group of fragile X children, called mosaics, who make limited stores of the crucial protein (which is called FMR1), are considerably higher functioning than those who don't. They may have mild learning problems and social unease, but they generally learn to read and write tolerably well and, as adults, to hold a job. As protein levels drop, though, so does performance, and in children with none at all the news is grim. "The impairment occurs throughout the brain, and in the networks in the brain that solve problems," says Dr. Randi Hagerman, medical director of the M.I.N.D. Institute at the University of California, Davis, and author of the definitive fragile X text, *Fragile X Syndrome.* "When you add other problems in the hypothalamus, which coordinates and fine-tunes the nervous system, you get a pretty clear sense of why they're besieged. The volume's turned up to 10 inside, and they can't turn it down."

In that neurological tumult it's all a kid can do to tolerate being around others, so fixed is he on dumping the energy coursing through his nervous system. Fragile X toddlers, or "fraggles," as my wife calls them, often flap their arms wildly at their sides and bounce on the balls of their feet. They screech rather than talk, emitting a high-pitched squeal that's a menace to eardrums, if not windows. They're virtually incapable of sitting still, twisting and gnashing and chewing their hands till the webbing is calloused and bruised. A change in routine can cause panic, a trip to the shoe store pure suffering. Vacations, even brief ones, are out of the question, triggering in some kids such nervous-system havoc that they can lapse into prolonged seizures. I know of few X-ers over the age of 9 who are not on a high-test regimen of drugs, including an adult-strength sedative, a mood pill such as Zoloft, and a stimulant from the Ritalin family. Additionally many take anticonvulsants and top things off with an antipsychotic, such as Risperdal or Seroquel. Even on such a cocktail they are prone to the sort of freakouts that make parents rue their own birth.

"The drugs do help, but better ones are needed, and I'm excited by what's in the pipeline," says Hagerman, who began treating X-ers in the early 1980s, when the condition was named. "Things like ampakines, which are in human trials, seem to enhance memory and learning. And though it's several years from being ready for humans, there's a class of drugs that work on the glutamate system that may have a far-ranging impact on the lives of these kids as well as on those of Alzheimer's and seizure patients. But the holy grail, of course, would be replacing the FMR1 protein, which would have the greatest impact on fragile X children."

It's the first fine Sunday in a leaden April, and we're out with our son early at a packed Brooklyn playground. Though he's been up since a quarter of 4—again—Luke charges away from me when he sees the swings, darting in front of a bus as we cross the street. He lacks all sense of ambient danger, and if left to his own devices would camp in the crosswalk for a better look at the cars.

My wife bundles him into a toddler swing and takes the first shift pushing him high. Like me, Elaine is haggard and in a filthy mood; neither of us has slept much in days. As a young mom next to her bills and coos, flirting with a baby dressed in Big Bird yellow, Elaine glares murder at the middle distance, perhaps seeing my face in the trees. Five years ago we were sailing through life, the road ahead open for miles. We rarely, if ever, argued, had lots of avid sex, and on weekends slept till the crack of noon, when hunger—or boredom—roused us. Now we go for days barely speaking at all, and we often sleep, if that's the word for it, in separate beds. Each of us has aged a decade in those years, our joints and spirits cracking with fatigue. Occasionally our eyes meet in a moment of dolor, as if to ask the other, How did we get here?

"I'm going to buy juice," she says, meaning, "Your turn." This is how we talk now, in a kind of semaphore.

I take over, pushing him higher and higher, a touch, perhaps, of malice in the act. But if Luke is aware of his parents' oppression, his demeanor gives no hint of it. Today, as always, he's in great form: cheerful, tireless, and in love with the world—or, at any rate, with his insular piece of it. Like a lot of other X kids he has a motor that won't quit, going all week on minimal rest before he crashes in a 12-hour stupor. (It's thought that the part of the brain that runs the circadian rhythm is disabled in fragile X, a theory backed by studies in mice.) But unlike many X kids he's weirdly serene, a joy at all hours (except 4 a.m.). At William O'Connor-Bay Ridge, a wonderfully humane preschool for special needs kids of all kinds, he is hugely popular with teachers and classmates, though he has next to no language and even less interest in relating to other kids. Seldom a month passes without a proposal of marriage from some 3-year-old ingénue he met at the park, or a fight breaking out between two of his playmates over who will open his juice box. Still, for all his sweetness I know the clock is ticking and that soon these 4-year-olds will turn 5, then 6, and ask the kinds of questions native to 6-year-olds everywhere: What's wrong with that kid? Is he retarded?

Elaine comes back from the bagel store with a bag of fresh-made doughnuts. It's exactly the sort of kindness she used to toss off idly, before we became accountants of parental toil, tracking who got up more often with Luke and who had the last night out. That speaks to the childishness that exhaustion spawns, but it's also a register of something poisonous, namely an apportionment of blame. Our lives are in havoc; we're furious about it and burn to hold someone or something responsible for this colossal trick of fate. We've tried hating the doctors who failed for years to correctly diagnose Luke, the hospital for failing to test for fragile X during the standard prenatal screening, and the insurance companies for their mingy, corporate-minded refusal to pay for such a test. (That $200 bit of blood work could have saved them real money: It costs upward of $2 million to care for an X-er over the course of his or her lifetime.)

But when you're up before dawn for the fifth night running, or surrounded in the park by precocious kids while your child can't say his own name, the hunt for scapegoats doesn't range much farther than the person standing beside you. No marriage can withstand that sort of deadening grudge, and we are both in counseling to find a way past it, to hold our home together till help arrives. After months of acrid wrangling about medication—me for, she against—we've come to an agreement, dosing Luke first with a sedative at nighttime, then, in due time, with Zoloft during the day. It's a serious step when you consider his age, but we're past the point of half measures, of herbal baths and craniosacral work. There's no firm number for fragile X parents, but the divorce rate for all couples with special needs kids is between 80 and

90 percent, or nearly double that of the general population. And if the two of us combined are no match for Luke, I shudder to think how we'd manage apart, with no backup at 4 a.m.

After a half-hour of swinging, Luke crosses his arms, his chosen signal for finished. As I reach to unbuckle him he pulls me close, seizing my neck in a hug. I stand there, love-drunk, soaking him in, imbibing his warmth and little-boy scent, his ineffable, head-swimming charm. There is magic in my son, and I'm not alone in saying so. By some combination of beauty and temperament he affects virtually everyone he comes into contact with, including bus drivers, matrons, and lunchroom attendants. This summer he'll graduate from his fourth preschool, and if the scene there is anything like the other three, there won't be enough tissues to go around. At last year's ceremony his teacher and her assistant had to duck inside a classroom to have a cry, and they barely managed to croak out their farewells. Only an ogre could begrudge this child, and yet these days my fantasies involve time without him—specifically, the time before his birth.

We were living in a triplex loft back then, with sweeping ceilings, 12-foot windows, and—that needle in a New York haystack—a parking spot. We were both in our 40s, had flourishing careers, and were comfortably resigned to childlessness after years of stop-and-start efforts. Then Elaine got pregnant the month her father died, and both of us took it as a blessing conferred, the passing of light to light. The delivery was long, though not dramatic, and as we brought Luke home from St. Luke's-Roosevelt, the drive down Broadway felt like a victory lap.

But with the curse of hindsight, it's clear to us now that something was wrong from day one. Luke wouldn't—or more properly, couldn't—take his mother's breast, and he lacked the motor strength to use a bottle. At 6 months he still couldn't roll himself over; at 9 months he didn't sit up. Alarmed, his doctor made a referral to a pediatric neurologist at New York University, who watched Luke fumble with tiny blocks and surmised that he had cerebral palsy. Tests were performed that neither proved that diagnosis nor ruled it out. We fired the neurologist and booked another, a star on the Upper East Side. She ordered further tests, including one we refused that involved 8-inch needles. As Luke turned 2 we got our second diagnosis: mild to moderate autism.

Though of some small help, at least with the insurance company, the label didn't fit our son. He laughed spontaneously; he loved us back; he mimicked Elmo and the Teletubbies by aping their ear-bleed screech. And so we pushed on, seeing a second internist and then a touted child psychologist. Both were stumped, hinting that we might never learn what hindered our son, the malfunctions of the brain being so abstruse as to conceal a pinpoint cause. Anyway, it was best to watch and wait; in a year, they said, the facts might show themselves.

As Luke approached 3 we all but gave up, coming to terms with his latest diagnosis: pervasive developmental disorder. It's a trashcan label, the doctor who made it readily confessed to us, used to lump together a broad range of kids whose defects stump clinicians. Though it came a bit closer to describing Luke, it offered not even a slender hope of a cure or useful treatment. By then he was finally up and walking, thanks to a fine program in Bay Ridge, Brooklyn, called, poignantly enough, Thursday's Child. Tailored to kids with major learning delays, the program taught Luke to connect with and navigate the world through a series of discrete trials and errors. He began uttering his first crude words there, and he worked like a demon with his therapists.

Then, when we'd stopped looking for it, came our eureka moment, though in retrospect we were happier not knowing. Pressed by Luke's doctor, we paid a grudging visit to our third—and last—neurologist. She took one look at Luke's oval face and blurted out, "fragile X."

"Come again?" said my wife, who'd long since lost patience with doctors who addressed us as if we were colleagues.

"Yeah, a mutation of the X chromosome," said the neurologist. "Besides Down syndrome it's the leading cause of mental retardation. Have blood drawn and see me in six months."

Several nights later—on the eve of July 4, when anyone we might reasonably call for support had gone out of town for the weekend—the neurologist phoned to confirm. "It isn't every doctor who'd stay around late to break the news to you," she brayed. My hand went numb; I dropped the phone. I could hear her tinny patter coming up from the floor. When I grabbed the receiver again I screamed obscenities till my lungs, and balance, gave out. By then, though, I was talking to a dial tone, and my child was sobbing in terror down the hall.

In the weeks and months following the diagnosis Elaine free-dived the fragile X depths, and seldom rose for air. She read every word in the research journals, nagged Luke's therapists to spend their time likewise, and logged long hours corresponding with frantic parents on list-serve sites. Because she was constantly in motion—and I was fogged by grief—I didn't spot her enveloping despair until it had all but swallowed her whole. Formerly unsinkable, she now sobbed over trifles and struggled to get out of bed each day, racked with vagrant pains. One night, after a spat at the dinner table, it all came tumbling out of her: She had broken Luke's brain, he would always be helpless, and someday she would die and leave him.

"I'll be an old hag crossing the street with him, still holding his hand when he's 40," she sobbed. "Who'll look after him and keep him safe? I could go down in a plane tomorrow."

This was in the months following 9/11, and clearly her heartbreak was trading feedback with the hysteria of the day. But it doesn't take a degree in psychology to know that guilt had a part in this too. For all her new acumen in genetic transmission, Elaine was convinced that the gene had mutated in her. That was impossible: The defect builds slowly, growing by increments over many generations until it blooms into full mutation. Still, she kept running the grim statistics: If only she had dealt Luke her healthy X, which he'd had a 1-in-2 chance of getting; if only she'd given birth to a girl, who'd have had a 2-in-3 chance of dodging symptoms.

A lot of this I've learned from her over the past few months; at the time she was researching fragile X she was too embattled to even broach the subject. Nor, out of care for her aging mother, had she shared the news with her extended family, consoled by the knowledge that all the boys she knew were well. Then one day it dawned on her that she was missing half the picture: There could be women on her father's side who were carriers too. A letter went out to her paternal relations, urging them to take the test. Sure enough, a first cousin turned up positive, though the gene had spared her two children. For Elaine that finding seemed to ease the load, this retiring the matter of her own inheritance and with it some of her guilt.

"It wasn't just my father who had the premutation: His brother had to have had it too, and both of them had to have gotten it from their mom," she says, "which leads me to wonder, first, how long it had been hiding before it surfaced in me, and second, how many other women out there are about to pass on that first full mutation?"

If anyone out there is going to fix my child, it will be a woman like Katie Clapp. She isn't a neuroscientist or a biotech mogul but an unpedigreed housewife in Newburyport, Massachusetts, who won't take no for an answer. Ten years ago she and her husband, Michael Tranfaglia, a psychiatrist, got the hard news about their 3-year-old Andy, to which they numbly replied, "Fragile what?" Like my wife and me, they'd been trekking from doctor to doctor, bringing their son to prestigious specialists who should have known better. Unlike us, though, they had grounds for a lawsuit: During the years they were seeking a diagnosis they were told over and over that whatever Andy had, their next child wasn't at risk. And then they had Laura, who, within weeks of her birth, tested positive for the full mutation. (Thanks to good luck, and her second X chromosome, she is mercifully free of symptoms.)

But instead of suing experts up and down the coast, they plowed their outrage into something generative, starting a nonprofit called Fragile X Research Foundation (FRAXA). The foundation had, from its inception in 1994, a couple of bright-line goals: one, to spread the word about fragile X syndrome to doctors and parents worldwide, and two, to raise a large pot of money fast and fund a search for effective treatments and a cure. By 2002 they'd raised $7 million, most of it from the families of fragile X kids, and were underwriting dozens of research studies that have advanced the science by leaps. En route they pooled resources with other fragile X parents—Debbie Stevenson, the wife of a Wall Street baron; David Busby, a powerhouse Beltway lobbyist; and Kathy May, a player in the nonprofit sector—to turn up the heat on Congress.

When the group first appeared before the National Institutes of Health, government spending on fragile X research was less than $2 million annually. Eight years later it was more than $15 million, including funding for three new research centers whose sole purpose is to find a treatment and cure. But Clapp, who is FRAXA's one employee, was just rolling up her sleeves.

"When we first got the news about our son, then learned that all of five people in the entire world were investigating the gene, I said, 'No way, this will not stand. Someone has to help these kids,'" she says, sitting on the deck of her trim colonial on a cul-de-sac in this seaport town. "That was 9 years ago, and we've built the field since, recruiting Nobel laureates, National Academy scientists, and Howard Hughes Medical Institute investigators. And thanks to them, and to the 6,000 people in our network, we stumbled onto a major find: a class of drugs that's going to change all this. It's still in mouse trials and will probably cost $10 million just to bring before the FDA. But I'll get that money somewhere if I have to beg, borrow, or steal—and anyone who says different doesn't know me."

Tranfaglia, her husband, laughs. He's the cool clinician to her firebrand, the guy who works behind the scenes to nudge the research ahead. He's also, by default, the consulting physician to families around the country, freely helping desperate fragile X parents get the right mix of drugs for their kids. It is vastly complex and can take months or years to find a regimen that calms down a child. But Tranfaglia can count on one hand the number of psychiatrists who are knowledgeable about X-ers, and so he takes the 3 a.m. phone calls from parents at the end of their rope.

"What Katie's talking about is a class of drugs called mGluR5 antagonists," Tranfaglia says. "In fragile X mice it stops lab-induced seizures 100 percent of the time and also dampens the neuroreceptors that trigger panic and obsessive-compulsion. Then other people found that when mice take it in large doses it blocks addiction, not just to cocaine but to a whole class of opiates and stimulants. Within a decade it'll revolutionize substance abuse treatment and be the drug of choice for Parkinson's and epilepsy and a range of anxiety symptoms. But we can't wait 10 years. Our son has almost died three times."

Andy, whose picture is everywhere in the house, is now a handsome boy of 14. Like a quarter of all kids with fragile X he suffers from a form of seizure disorder, though his is more dire than most. Just one missed dose of anticonvulsants can induce an event called *status epilepticus*, in which he seizes until he's treated or dies. The last such seizure was nearly fatal; it occurred during a trip to a neuroscience conference and cured his mom of trips for a while.

"Our whole focus now is to find a biotech firm that will underwrite the cost of the drug trials," she says. "Once one's ready to be tested in human subjects, and if we can get the feds to treat it as an orphan drug [i.e., indicated for a small class of potential users], we could bring it to market in 3 years. A small start-up company that's willing to roll the dice would have things to itself for 5 to 7 years and could make hundreds of millions of dollars for its trouble. They would also earn my undying gratitude, and the gratitude of millions of families."

We talk a while longer about mGluR5's properties, and how it goes to work on the neuropathways, aping the FMR1 protein. (Researchers have produced a synthetic version of the protein but are years away from having a sense of how to deploy it.) Tranfaglia is sketching out glutamate receptors when a bus pulls up to the drive. Down steps a slender, auburn-haired boy with a bashful, meandering gait. He walks in the door, takes a look at me, and instantly begins to shake. My heartbeat skitters as he drops his pants, the preface to a full-on scene. But his mother glides to him and heads things off, parking Andy in the living room with his dinner and a video. When Clapp returns her hands are trembling as she pours herself a drink.

"That's why we put in 60-hour weeks and haven't taken a vacation in 10 years. It's not that we're saints whose mission is to save these kids. We're out here trying to save *our* kid, and if we happen to save yours, too, more's the better."

It is night four of our own drug trials, and nights one through three went beautifully. On a mild combination of an antihypertensive and the over-the-counter sleep-aid melatonin, Luke slept soundly from 9 p.m. till his wake-up at a quarter of 7. Neither Elaine nor I can bring ourselves to raise the subject and tiptoe around it like the teammates of a pitcher who's throwing a perfect game. So when I click off the tube and head down to bed, it is with a certain amount of giddy stealth, lest I somehow tempt the fates. Sure enough, at 3:15, a loud thump wakes me. Fearing the worst, I race up the steps, expecting to find Luke in a druggy heap after tumbling out of bed. But when I open his door, it's the cat who's spooked, having knocked over a See 'n' Say toy. Luke is snoring softly into the trunk of his stuffed elephant; as usual, one of his socks has gone missing. I kneel down, ostensibly to straighten the sheets, but find myself suddenly in prayer.

Please, I say to whoever's listening.

Please, please, please, I beg you.

X Marks The Spot

Tracey Franks is the president of the Fragile X Society of Arizona and the mother of a 7-year-old boy with fragile X and autism.

All of the expectations still loom in the back of my mind

Remembering the day that they told me, he was more than a little behind.

He looks at me with great beauty, and always a glistening eye

As if he knows there's a problem, and he is looking and asking "why?"

All of the answers he's wanting are still questions I ask inside

Trying to find the answers, the emotion I'm trying to hide.

—Mindy Wagner

March 10, 2005: Maricopa County Superior Court

The marriage vows "for better or for worse" are a huge promise to make and it's a lot easier to focus on the "for better" side of life. It was difficult for me to admit my marriage of 12 years was far from

30

perfect—and even more difficult to end it. There we were sitting amidst the dark wood walls and studded leather chairs of a courtroom to hash out the financial details and leave the emotional ones unresolved. We had joined the thousands of marriages that fail when a special needs child is in the family.

"If you get nervous, just take a few deep breaths," was the advice my attorney offered as we stood in the cold, stark hallway preparing to enter the courtroom. Considering all I had been through the last 6 years, I was surprised at how anxiety was getting the better of me in this situation. Then again, my future and the future of my son was at stake and would probably end up in the hands of a judge who knew nothing of our lives, short of what I was about to say on the witness stand.

September 2000: A Diagnosis

"The doctor said something strange today," my husband remarked after returning from a visit to the pediatrician for yet another ear infection. Nicolas, our 20-month-old son, was fascinated with spinning objects, could hardly look you in the eye, and communicated primarily through screaming. All of this was running through my head when my husband went on to say, "The first thing the doctor said to me when she walked into the exam room was, 'You're not considering having more children, are you?'" I looked up from the potatoes I was chopping with a sick feeling in my stomach. There must be something seriously wrong with our son.

"She said he has fragile X syndrome, whatever that is," my husband continued, not knowing whether to be alarmed or simply concerned. The doctor had given him no information that he could remember. I tried to recall what the developmental pediatrician had told me months earlier when he suggested blood tests for several disorders. He said that he didn't think my son was autistic but felt "there's something else going on." Despite my protests that we didn't have any "strange cousins" or other genetic anomalies in our family background, the doctor's hunch proved to be correct.

31

After finishing dinner and putting our son to bed, my husband and I jumped on the Internet in a frantic search for information. We managed to find more than we could digest. One Web site condemned our son to a life of institutionalized care, while another said he could simply have learning disabilities. At the time, it was difficult not to focus on the worst-case scenario. We stayed up all night obsessing about our son's future and the shattered dreams we now faced. Our sobbing came from deep within—intense grief rolled over us like waves pounding the shore. Just when we thought we had caught our breath, another wave would roll in, knocking us to our knees. It's an emotion I carry with me to this day, but bury back in the depths of my soul. It escapes in measured doses but, uncontained, has the potential to send me to an emotional point of no return.

We learned that fragile X syndrome is the most common genetic cause of mental impairment in the world. It's called fragile X because, under a microscope, the X chromosome looks broken, or fragile, at the bottom. This chromosomal problem inhibits a protein from being produced in the brain and can result in mental retardation, autistic behaviors, learning disabilities, and physical characteristics such as a long face and prominent ears. About one in 750 men and one in 250 women are carriers. I was a carrier and didn't know it. Few carriers do. A family could go on for generations creating typical children. My father was a carrier who passed his carrier status on to me. As a woman, I have two X chromosomes. As a fragile X carrier, one of my two X chromosomes is flawed. My son, Nicolas, got the flawed one that mutated into full-blown fragile X in his body. It was a roll of the dice in a genetics game I had no idea I was playing.

Father Time

I never knew my biological father. My mother hates it when I say that, but I really have no recollection of the person who would occasionally come to see me as a toddler. He and my mother never married, a scandal in the 1960s, and went on to have another child who was given up for adoption 2 years after I was born. I never really thought any of that was important—I certainly felt complete as a person—until after Nicolas's diagnosis when my mother tested negative for fragile X carrier status. It didn't come from her but was passed to me through my father, a person I never felt the desire to know. Now something about him had changed my life and I wanted to know this man. Suddenly, I felt his blood running through my veins.

Dealing with Nicolas's issues and working full time, I barely had time to breathe, let alone look for my father. My mother hired a private detective who turned up a few dead-end leads. It didn't help that my father had an extremely common name, Richard Johnson. But that wasn't the reason he was so hard to find. He had dropped off the radar—he was living off the grid. My father was homeless.

What a private detective wasn't able to do, a Web search was. Frustrated by her lack of success in using more traditional avenues, my mother got on the Internet and Googled for Web sites to help locate people. Using my father's name and approximate date of birth, she posted a message on a site for missing persons, saying she was looking for him. The next morning she received an anonymous e-mail that said, "I'm sorry to tell you that he passed away in February 2003. He died at the Pleasant Care Convalescent Hospital." The e-mail also provided my father's exact date of birth. My mother replied, thanking the e-mailer for the information but never found out who provided her with the elusive information we needed.

Because my parents weren't married, my mother could not legally obtain any of my father's records. The anonymity of the Internet worked in her favor again as she typed in my personal information and got a copy of my father's death certificate from a vital records Web site. She never told me she was doing this. When she visited us in Phoenix several months later, she casually mentioned she had some news about my father and brought me outside to the patio. I looked down at the piece of paper that said my father was dead. For a moment I was numb, not sure what to feel. The "indigent" stamp boldly displayed at the top of the page finally triggered my tears.

A few days later, with my father's death certificate in hand, I called the coroner's office. I listened to the distant ring on the other end of the phone. I explained my situation to the woman who answered and asked if there were any records she could fax to me. Given that it had been over a year since my father died, she said she would have to go down to the basement and look for the official report. We hung up. Ten minutes later, my fax machine was slowly spitting out the pages. I spotted words like "past alcohol abuse," "dementia," and "cerebrovascular accidents" as they rolled by. But one sentence hit me harder than the rest: *The decedent had no next of kin listed in his records, nor any other assets, last will, or burial instructions. The decedent's Bank of America account has only $2.75.*

My father had died alone and penniless. He never knew I was looking for him, or that anyone cared.

Real Life

Ironically, I had no desire to have children until I was in my early 30s. Friends laughed at my lack of maternal instincts. Even the calmest baby would scream when I picked it up. However, I knew when I got married that my husband would make a terrific father. We tried for a year to get pregnant with no luck. Premature ovarian failure, or POF, is common in fragile X carriers. Of course my doctor, when he suggested a low-dose fertility drug, didn't know I carried the fragile X premutation, or had POF. I conceived but miscarried at ten weeks. I should have listened to my intuition. Within six months I was pregnant again.

As an infant, Nicolas was fussy and never slept more than two hours at a time. He would go from happy to screaming in the blink of an eye. Even though I had to get up at 4 a.m. to work on a trading desk in those days, I relished the thought of a few hours away from him. Other mothers would wax nostalgic about how precious their time was with their babies, and all I could think about was how little I was enjoying it. I began to question whether I was a good mother, considering how unhappy my child was most of the time. At one point in my mental and physical exhaustion, I told my husband, "I can't do this anymore." I had dreams of handing over my son to someone who could.

When Nicolas was 9 months old, we took him to a Gymboree class and noticed how different he was from the other babies. He had no interest in the bubbles floating in the air, couldn't clap his hands to the music, and was virtually unaware of the other babies around him. We told his pediatrician our concerns, and she suggested we give it some time. A few weeks later, we were out running errands and stopped at Home Depot. Everyone could hear Nicolas's screams throughout the store—until we approached the ceiling fan department. It was as if a switch went off in his head, and he immediately calmed down as he focused on the rotating paddles. For many autistic children, watching spinning objects is like heroin to a junkie. It's impossible to get enough, and in Nicolas's case, it gave him great pleasure. When I mentioned this to my closest friend—a child psychologist—she calmly urged me to get him evaluated.

A parade of therapists came through our house to assess Nicolas's development. They asked me questions like, "Does he point to things?" and "How does he play with toy cars?" Somehow, I knew that "He turns the cars over and spins the wheels" wasn't a good answer, even if it was true. Too many times I had to answer "No" when they asked about Nicolas's ability to do something. His hyperactivity made the evaluations even more difficult because he couldn't focus on anything, even for a minute, unless there was music or movement involved. Soon after the evaluations were completed, we began an early intervention program that included speech, physical, occupational, and music therapies.

When he was nearly 3 years old, Nicolas became eligible to attend a special needs preschool. We scoured the Phoenix metro area searching for the best possible placement, even flying in a fragile X specialist from Denver for the day to make the rounds with us. The public school district that offered the best classroom for Nicolas wasn't the one we lived in. Open enrollment wasn't an option for this specialized program, so we sold our dream house to get him a coveted spot. That decision paid off tremendously in what Nicolas has been able to accomplish both behaviorally and cognitively. He spent 3 years in that nurturing preschool environment with teachers and therapists who patiently figured out how to teach him. On Nicolas's last day in preschool, the aide who shadowed him throughout each day handed me a card as tears filled her eyes. It read, "I am so glad that your son came into my life. He will always be in my heart. I believe that Nicolas has made me a better person. Thank you for letting me be a part of his life." Tears filled my eyes as I thanked her for the touching note, but my tears fell also because I knew my son would be lucky to find such dedicated professionals again.

The following year, during the first parent/teacher conference, the kindergarten speech therapist said matter-of-factly, "Now, you don't expect him to speak, do you?" Nicolas's father and I were taken aback at her question and silently wondered why she bothered to work with him if her expectations were so low. His vocabulary was limited, but Nicolas demonstrated speech routinely at home. Several weeks later, when I went to observe in his classroom, I realized that he wasn't talking there because no one was talking to him. They didn't believe he was capable.

It's a constant battle to find educators and therapists who share the expectations we have for our son. Like many typical children, Nicolas needs to be challenged in his learning environment. Boredom results in unwanted behaviors. The "team" of professionals involved in his life number more than twenty people, and just as many have come and gone over the years. Tireless advocacy has helped Nicolas arrive at the place he is today—accomplishing things the experts told us he never would.

Public Life

"That's quite a handsome young man you have there," a man commented as Nicolas and I stepped out to the grocery store parking lot. With his big chocolate-brown eyes trimmed in dark lashes, olive skin, full lips and athletic build, Nicolas was the spitting image of his handsome father. Hoping it would end the conversation, I thanked the man.

"What's your name, son?" he continued, trying to make eye contact with Nicolas. I cringed watching my son ignore this nice man, knowing there would be no answer to the question. Quickly, I offered, "His name is Nicolas," and nervously joked about him being shy that day. I just didn't feel like explaining my son's behavior to yet another person out in public. It would be so much easier if he wore his disability on the outside instead of the inside.

Watching the cars in the parking lot, in his excitement Nicolas made one of his inappropriately loud noises. The man recoiled, as if Nicolas were contagious, and immediately looked horrified. Then he said, "Oh, I'm sorry." I wanted to snap, "There's nothing to be sorry for," but instead I quietly walked away. At least I didn't get the endless questions I sometimes get from people who think it's a game to figure out what's wrong with my kid. I prefer the occasional knowing smile or glance from someone who understands. In that moment of camaraderie, I don't feel so alone in the struggle.

As difficult as it can be, it's important to expose Nicolas to the world and the world to Nicolas. At the same time, it is a constant reminder to me of how different my child is. Most parents think nothing of shopping with their children, but for us, it is a well-choreographed outing that gets easier with time. Nicolas may be the only child who can walk into Toys R Us, spend 15 minutes looking around, and walk out empty-handed just as happy as when he walked in. I smile to myself as we walk by the typical children in the checkout line screaming about the toy they didn't get.

My smugness disappears at our next stop, the neighborhood park, as I watch other 6-year-olds playing tag—a game Nicolas doesn't yet understand. This reality feels like a slap in the face.

Why?

On bad days, the "why" questions are endless in my head: Why me? Why was Nicolas the one to get fragile X? Why has our life turned out this way? Over the years, my more religious friends have said things like, "You know, God gave you Nicolas for a reason," or "Everything will be fine. God doesn't give you more than you can handle." I realize these comments are meant to give me strength and maybe an answer to some of my why questions, but they really just irritate me.

In the traditional sense, I am not a religious person. I would classify my beliefs as more spiritual in nature. I don't draw strength or acceptance of my situation by placing its creation at the feet of a higher power. On any given day I'm the best judge of whether I can handle my life or not. On the other hand, I've learned that creating my destiny is only possible to a point. Sometimes I just have to go along for the ride.

The Future

Caring for Nicolas is an arduous, complicated, and continuous process. What happens today can have a significant impact on what happens in the future. He is truly a work in progress and a labor of love. His father loves him dearly but has never come to terms with a son who is different than he imagined he would be. His pride in Nicolas's accomplishments is muted, and he holds a quiet hope for the future. Even though our marriage has ended, our partnership as parents will continue.

Having a child with a disability changed the very core of my being. I no longer need "things" to make me happy, or to live in an extravagant house like the one we once owned. Now true happiness is when my son leaves his Thomas the Train video to give me a hug. Our emotional connection was many years in the making, and it is something I cherish.

There isn't anything I wouldn't do for the chance to cure my son. Until then, giving Nicolas the best shot at an independent life is what drives me. It's a role I never thought I would be in, but one that I have come to accept. Learning to celebrate things other parents take for granted is utterly humbling. When Nicolas looks at me with loving eyes, softly pats me on the back and says "Baby," I know he means "I love you, baby," but he can't get all the words out. I live for the day that he does.

A Fragile Strength

Susan Cohen is a literary agent in New York and has a son with fragile X syndrome.

The simple yet miraculous act of childbirth makes you fragile. After the pain comes the postpartum exhaustion and hormonal sensitivity. Then the now-that-we've-got-him-home-what-do-we-do insecurity. The sleep-deprived haze. Concern that this little crying creature must be pretty fragile. Concern in our case that he wasn't catching on—or latching on—to breast-feeding. The weight all parents feel of this new lifelong responsibility. But all of that is a kind of elated fragility. And all of that was when we thought our son was perfect.

Then came the phase of beginning to feel less fragile, like maybe we were capable of being parents after all. But that was soon undercut by our pediatrician's suspicion that something was wrong. We preferred to believe those who pooh-poohed her concerns. Exams were done and blood was tested. And when Julian was nearly 2, we got the fairly shattering confirmation that there was in fact something wrong. And it had an odd name: fragile X syndrome.

We hadn't heard of fragile X when we got the diagnosis. Looking it up on the Internet didn't soften the blow. In our first research, we learned more than we wanted to, and quickly went from ignorance to depression. With myriad evaluations and applications, we amassed more paperwork than we could have imagined. I put it all in what I called "The X Files."

At first I thought the diagnosis would make *me* forever fragile. That I'd be too sad about my son's future to accept it. Too ill-equipped to handle his altered existence—or mine. That without a cure or treatment, he'd be helpless—and so would we. And at first, I guess, I was pretty fragile.

I tried to see beyond that first depressing phase. I didn't want to look too far into his murky future. But I told people before really believing it myself that at some point I'd just accept it as one of Julian's features: blond hair, blue eyes, fragile X. And I soon knew, in both my head and my heart, that we had to accept and value him for what he *is*—rather than what he couldn't be.

I also came to see that he was such a happy kid it seemed inappropriate for us to be depressed. He enjoyed life a lot, and mostly made us laugh. At age 10, he still does.

His fragile X in fact made *me* not fragile, but stronger. Parenthood for many people brings out strengths we didn't know we had. Having a challenging child challenges the parent to meet the special needs. And our son seems to be so charming and so category-defying to teachers, therapists, and case managers that my husband, Barry, likes to say, "he puts the *Special* in Special Ed."

We'll never be able to change Julian that much. But I'm not sure we'd want to. Barry reported that at a fathers' group he attended at the 9th National Fragile X Conference, the men were asked if they'd give their kids a drug if it would "cure" them. Many said no or had real hesitations. Because of Julian's enthusiasm for life, Barry feels that instead of our trying to make this unique kid more like us, the world would be a better place if we were all more like Julian.

Which brings me to the worst things people said to me when we were first grappling with the diagnosis. Admittedly, for a while it seemed that there was no right thing people could say. I really was fragile. I didn't believe the hollow reassurances that "he'll be fine." I didn't appreciate the well-intentioned but patronizing, "God only gives special children to special parents." And I cried at the left-handed compliment: "Oh sure, he's a great kid. But can you imagine what he'd be like if he *didn't* have fragile X?"

But the most painful remark was made by the mother of an old friend: "You're just upset because he's not like *you*." I didn't know how true it might be, but I hated hearing it. I realized later that she was still upset about learning that her otherwise perfect son was gay—projecting her own disappointment, despite all his other sterling qualities, that her eldest child's lifestyle wouldn't mirror hers.

Well, 8 years after Julian's diagnosis, after all those early, insensitive remarks, do I still feel fragile? No. I feel stronger and wiser. A telling difference was that in the first year of being a fragile X parent, when I heard about the National Fragile X Foundation's biannual conference, I thought: "What could be more depressing than talking about it for four days and hanging around with other depressed parents?" Two years later, I found the idea—and the reality—quite energizing. It was great to spend time soaking up information both scientific and anecdotal. We began to bond with parents and professionals who now feel like our extended family. I've since taken on tasks to raise both funds and awareness, accomplishments which have also been quite rewarding.

And it's not just my perspective about fragile X that's changed. It's my whole view of parenthood. I see and hear things differently now. And lots of people have started saying lots of right things.

Julian's condition has caused me to examine myself and others in ways I wouldn't have thought of doing if it hadn't been for him. It's made me realize how narrow the criteria of parental pride can be, if we buy into society's expectations. While I never equated material success with happiness, I did grow up judging people by how smart they were. That was hard to let go. When I heard a friend's description of a young man whose IQ was off the charts but who was miserable, I decided I'd rather have a happy kid with a below-average IQ. It may be a rationalization, but I find I feel liberated from the pressures and competition of upper middle-class overachievers. An odd kind of smugness! One charming upper-class fragile X mother I know joked that if her kids had been able to go to the most elite private schools, she and her husband would have been "insufferable snobs." So, fragile X also keeps you humble.

On the other hand, it lends greater significance to the word "pride." We so appreciate each delayed milestone Julian reaches—progress most parents take for granted. And even his immaturity has its upsides. Other parents complain about how quickly their kids grow up. You won't hear that at our house! Other kids stop being goofy and affectionate at a young age; Barry and I are spoiled by a very amusing and still-snuggly boy.

We've also become card-carrying members of a club we didn't want to join. Learned to do things we didn't know we'd have to do. Met terrific people we'd never have known, parents and teachers and professionals in occupations I didn't know existed. I'll admit we've taken guilty comfort, at special-needs parent support groups, hearing about kids who are worse off. We've felt relief to discover other fragile X parents with the same frustrations—particularly when we realize our kid is past a phase others are still in. We're glad to reassure their parents they'll eventually get through it too. We're happy when we see older kids with fragile X doing really well, and grateful for all the caring people—family, friends, educators, and therapists—who have provided many kinds of support. We're constantly telling each other how lucky we are.

So in fact we feel far from fragile. Sometimes Julian's difficulties leave us frazzled. Often we're confused by different, even competing options. (More or less inclusion at school? Does he need medication?) But all parents get frazzled and confused. And there's rarely one right answer when it comes to the choices all parents make. Occasionally I get wistful when I see what typical kids are up to, doing things that maybe Julian won't ever do. But on the whole, being his mother has made me stronger. I think it's made my husband stronger. Perhaps even strengthened our marriage. Through all the additional tasks and topics Julian's condition has made us tackle, we generally concur, occasionally disagree, roll up our sleeves, roll our eyes, laugh a lot, sigh sometimes, but hardly ever cry.

One of the things that did depress me and make me feel fragile again was when I would take Julian to visit my father. He'd been diagnosed with multiple sclerosis and spent the last 5 years of his life in a nursing home, a shadow of his former self. He virtually stopped talking. And so I'd sit in a room with a nonverbal father and a speech-delayed son. A grandfather who couldn't really play with his long-awaited first grandchild. A son who couldn't imagine the answer when I asked him who *my* daddy was.

A year or so after my father died, we realized that he probably suffered from fragile X-associated tremor ataxia syndrome (FXTAS), a set of symptoms caused by the premutation whose full-blown form causes fragile X syndrome. We believe now that my father had FXTAS instead of MS, or maybe in addition to it. For both my mother and me, that knowledge brought some clarity to my father's decline, and a surprising feeling not of comfort but closure. It made more sense to us that we'd been hit by two forms of one debilitating condition rather than two entirely different ones. Because I hadn't known I was a carrier, I hadn't felt guilt about being the parent who gave our son fragile X, just as I wouldn't have blamed my husband if he'd had the mutation and passed it on to a daughter. But now I feel a twinge of guilt if the mutation skipped from my father to my son without affecting me (at least so far).

Do I wish my son didn't have fragile X? Of course. Would I have pushed for another child if I weren't a carrier? Probably. Do I worry about Julian's future? If I let myself focus on it. And have I started believing the cliché of taking life one day at a time? I sure have.

But I don't feel unlucky. And I no longer feel fragile. I truthfully tell Julian all the time that I'm glad to be his mom. I once joked with some fragile X parents at a meeting, when we'd all exchanged funny stories about the odd things our "fraggles" had done, that they might be weird, but it was a *fun* kind of weird.

Because of Julian's one fragile-looking X chromosome, the word *fragile* has taken on new meanings in my life. One of them is "strength."

All Possible Worlds

*Julie L. Peters, an assistant professor of history at the
University of Illinois at Chicago, is the mother of a 5-year-old
with fragile X syndrome.*

Before our son was born my husband and I wondered—what would
we teach this child? What would we teach him about Santa Claus?
Would we tell him the truth from the beginning or wean him slowly, or
just let him find out the way we did when we were children? What about
Jesus and God? What did we really believe anymore? We discussed
and dissected what we believed so that this child would have a fresh
fingerprint, free of what we had been raised to accept without question.
Colin would be a grand opportunity for us to do everything the way we
thought it should be done.

In this sense, the universe has a keen sense of humor. Or perhaps
a way of giving us exactly what we ask for. Because fragile X makes
most of our pre-child discussions seem poignant when we are grieving.
Other times they are just amusing.

Christmas is just another day. Santa and anticipation of his visit do
not exist. Advent calendars are pointless. Presents could sit unopened
forever because our child doesn't wonder what is inside and doesn't

care. And Jesus? Colin wouldn't know the name of his preschool teacher without reference to a picture and a direct experience with her, let alone a spiritual figure from two centuries ago. Birthdays are meaningless at best. At worst, they are frightening days when people light food on fire and put it in front of you while they stand very close to you and sing too loudly. As parents we walk through the paces so that we don't feel we are cheating him, or giving up, or perhaps in hopes that some of the socialization and ritual will rub off and make things seem more normal.

Before I go on, I want to be clear. I have nothing new to say about having a special needs child that other parents haven't felt or said before. Parents whose children have suffered and died may even envy me. This is an essay about sorrow and grieving, about joy and being at peace. I am in mourning. I am also Candide. Either I am making this the best of all possible worlds or I am seriously in denial, depending on how one looks at it and who is looking.

Parents of special needs children understand the process of letting go of the things they thought would be. Obvious "there-will-never-be" moments make the list. There will be no normal Little League, no prom, no wedding, no grandchildren. Actually, those are all things I can live without. It's the little things that make me sad, things I did as a child that I looked forward to doing with my son. There may be no bike-riding, ball-kicking, picture-coloring, spontaneous snowman-building, or lovely explanations of where clouds come from. Anything a normal child would do may not happen. All it takes is a trip to the park to have the differences one might never think of become glaringly apparent.

What makes fragile X a bit different is that these realizations often come slowly. When Colin was born, he was perfect. A bit jaundiced, but healthy. His Apgar scores were dead-on. Gradually we became somewhat concerned as milestones were missed, then more concerned, and then very. There were enough minutes and days that seemed normal to make us believe that eventually things would work themselves out and that everything would be fine. The diagnosis did not come until Colin was 4 years old. This delay prolonged the exhausting cycle of hope and despair. Getting the diagnosis was painful, but it did help begin the healing process. The first step was accepting the finality. This child will never be normal, no matter how many times he gets bounced on a therapy ball. It is like death in that way. There is nothing, absolutely nothing, I can do to change it or stop it or make it go away.

Enter Candide, who despite overwhelming adversity tried to find a positive side to it all. This is a tricky role for parents of special needs children. You can begin to sound like a bad greeting card or a really pathetic self-help book. To teachers and school administrators you can sound like you are in denial. Even to yourself you can sound trivial and false. But it is here that I have found fragile X to be a very important teacher. There is opportunity in loss like this, a chance to reexamine and reconsider everything. There are useful lessons in pain if one chooses to study them. You can decide to try and make the best of it or you can decide to stay in grief. Most days have a bit of each.

There are gifts along every step of this journey of reexamination. And I would return every single one of them if I had the chance. I do not want these gifts. Without hesitation I would trade them all if Colin could be normal, but I cannot. Thus, a new list of nots and nevers.

My child is not in pain. He is not dying. He is not restrained by braces or tubes. He does not have seizures. He is not deformed or physically marred—in fact, he is really quite beautiful. Except for when he cannot utter a single word to express himself he is mostly a happy little boy. Often times he is joyful and completely exuberant.

My son will never be a soldier sent off to die in war. He will never be a drunken driver who kills another child. He will not make national headlines as a corrupt corporate giant whose greed ruined the lives of millions. He will not steal our money or deal drugs to schoolchildren. It is unlikely that he will ever do anything to intentionally break our hearts, scandalize our name, destroy our hopes, or hurt another person. Since he does not imitate for the sake of imitation, he will probably not go along with a group even though he knows the group is wrong. He will not forsake his own personality or safety or values in order to fit in. He probably won't make fun of a handicapped child on the playground.

Our grief is largely felt upfront. We already know about most of the things he will not achieve and we also have the gift of knowing the kinds of grief we have been spared. I read about these kinds of tragedies in the news and I am grateful for what I will never have to lose.

The blessings of fragile X syndrome would be well recognized in several religions. If you believe in reincarnation as a process whereby the soul is gradually freed of sin and material desires, my son's soul is in very good shape. He is not greedy. He covets nothing. Each day is new and full of very small pleasures. Tomorrow, let alone next week or the afterlife, are all concepts far too abstract for him to understand. These ideas will probably develop later in life, but I sense they will never be very important to him. How many people struggle to achieve a timeless sense of the present? How hard do some people work to give up their desire for material things and to return to a probably unachievable state of simply being? If nothing else, Colin's soul is safe because of the ways he has been freed from being normal. He has no vanity. He does not care how he is dressed or what he looks like; he is the lily of the field that we are told to consider. He will be called "retard," and typically developing children are going to make a lot of fun of him but he will never do these things to others. He is in a state of grace.

This is very useful to remember when we are at the park or the swimming pool. It is painful to see typically developing children play and do without thinking what Colin cannot yet do. I marvel at how easy it is when everything goes right. Pointing, using language, creating games, digging sand with desire and great purpose like most toddlers do. I grieve the differences every day. To compensate, I wonder about the children I see. I wonder whether they will become good or bad people and what kind of sorrow or disappointment lies in store for their parents. I do not wish it on anyone but I think about it.

I see even very young children look curiously at my child when he jumps and flaps his hands, making monotone vowel sounds or shrieking with delight. I encourage him to hold a shovel to fill a bucket with sand and then release him when he resists. He does not see the point. I ask him to throw a ball to me. He doesn't want to. I cannot understand why everything is so foreign to him. Sometimes it seems like he has just landed from another planet. Why is everything he does so different? At these times I summon ethereal spiritual concepts like reincarnation, and I recall how fortunate he is, in the grand scheme of things, not to be like other children. How lucky I am! How good this is for Colin, really. I summon these thoughts and I pray them like a Rosary: Blessed am I among women. And blessed is the fruit of *my* womb, Colin. I pray something like this to keep the tears from welling up or to keep from losing my temper. Mostly I pray it so that he can never see in my eyes disapproval, or disappointment, or grief, because when he looks at me I think he
can tell.

Some positive things about having a child with fragile X syndrome: Developmental milestones happen in slow motion. When your child learns something he has struggled for years to master you don't miss it. We have come to see the wonder of each thing Colin has learned— drinking from a cup, using a spoon, understanding an abstract request without a visual cue. We sit in awe and we celebrate things that most parents probably take for granted because they can. We experience joy and we don't miss a thing.

There is also great freedom for parents of fragile X children. We probably don't have to save up for college. We are also free from worrying about high SAT scores or excellent grades, competing to get into magnet schools, or cheating. We don't have to worry whether he has mastered numbers and the alphabet well enough to get ahead in kindergarten. We won't be getting a personal trainer when Colin is in middle school so that he can compete for athletic scholarships. We'll be happy if he learns to ride a bicycle. The pressures that middle-class parents seem to impose upon themselves and their children are nothing to us. We threw out the "what to expect" books when Colin turned 2. It was clear by then that we were on a different track altogether.

We have learned to adjust our expectations to the most basic levels imaginable. Applications for social services ask us questions that force us to think as though we had never heard the words before. What do you want for your child? What do you hope for him to achieve?

These are profound questions. We should all ask them. What do you want? What are your goals? What do we all hope to become as human beings? It's an amazing opportunity to become very clear about the purpose of our existence.

The more I probe, the more I ask: Why? Why is this important? I want my child to be happy. What does this mean? I want him to be at peace. He often already is. I want him not to intentionally hurt anyone. I don't want him to be hurt by anyone else. Should he learn to work? Of course. But why? What values am I imposing and which ones are authentic? If he could be taken care of for the rest of his life, would work be important if he didn't want it? What should he do with his life? Why are we here? Why are we, each of us, here?

If we strip away every layer of what we give meaning, if we examine it based on how much it contributes to our purpose, we are not left with much that is important. Much of what makes us fully human does not necessarily make us good. Maybe everything we need to know really does get taught in kindergarten. If that's the case, then Colin is set. He should have most of that mastered by fifth grade. If a person doesn't want any more, is it important for us to want it for him?

I want him to love and to know that he is loved. He already does the first part and the rest is up to those who surround him. How freeing it is to search for life's meaning and to know that your child may be further along the path to fulfillment than you will ever be.

I want my child to learn to speak and to express his thoughts. He is severely apraxic and cannot tell us when he has had a bad dream or when his feelings have been hurt. This causes us great pain and it clearly causes Colin great frustration. Beyond this, I know that I wanted to have art come home from school so I could put it on the refrigerator. I have piles of this, thanks to the patience of his teachers who made most of it hand over hand.

I would still like to know where Colin thinks clouds come from. My husband and I wait in hope to hear his voice form words and tell us what he thinks about his life. It would be wonderful to hear what Colin wants for himself and what he thinks he is here to do.

In the meantime, all I can do is ask myself the same questions. What is the purpose of this and what good can come of it? Despite any possible spiritual benefits, I would not choose fragile X for my son or for anyone, but here it is. Acceptance and serenity are hard-won, and I wonder whether I will ever completely achieve them. It is a cliché to say that I will learn more from my child than he will learn from me, but it is probably true.

I am learning because of who my child is; perhaps this is part of his purpose. If so, then maybe my lesson is to simply accept life the way it is and to be grateful. Every gift comes with a price and few people get them all. I wish I had more to say but that's all I've come up with so far. I can only learn to be at peace by continuing to desperately love Colin, precisely for the way he has been given to us, not in spite of what he may never be.

Repeats

Claire Dunsford is associate dean in the College of Arts and Sciences at Boston College. She and three sisters are all carriers, and together they have four children with fragile X.

Trinucleotide, or triplet, repeats consist of 3 nucleotides consecutively repeated (e.g., CAG CAG CAG CAG) within a region of DNA....[S]ome do change in length when passed on, and when that occurs, the gene is often disrupted. This mutational type, first discovered in 1991, was termed a dynamic or expansion mutation.

> —Russell L. Margolis, "Genetics of Childhood Disorders: IX. Triplet Repeat Disorders," Journal of the American Academy of Child and Adolescent Psychiatry, Dec. 1999.

So be beginning, be beginning to despair.
O there's none; no no no there's none:
Be beginning to despair, to despair,
Despair, despair, despair, despair.

> —Gerard Manley Hopkins, "The Leaden Echo and the Golden Echo"

Maybe the hiccups could have tipped me off. While I was pregnant, I would frequently feel the baby hiccupping inside me; the feeling was hilarious, almost but not quite as if I were hiccupping myself. In the later months I would look down at my belly and actually see my skin twitch with each tiny convulsion.

It's funny how the phenotype of fragile X mirrors the genotype. The very essence of the syndrome lies in repetition run amok. The typical person has about 30 repeats of a section of DNA on the FMR1 gene that reads CGG: that is, CGGCGGCGGCGG 30 times. This happy person then passes on the same number of repeats to his or her offspring in what is known as a "stable" version of the gene. But some individuals are in what is known as a "grey zone," a place of instability, and carry 45 to 55 repeats, thus making them more likely to have children who have an even higher number of repeats. These unlucky children have 55 to 200 repeats and carry the premutation of the gene. Genetically more unstable still, they have a high risk of passing on a full mutation to their children, more than 200 repeats and up to as high as several thousand.

As an aesthetic category, repetition is pleasing. It makes possible poetry and song with their rhymes, meter, stanzas, and refrains; it marks the best oratory in the shape of anaphora. But when does repetition cease to please and start to annoy? When does a chime become a hammer? Any parent knows how children like repetition, the bedtime story told every night, the knock-knock joke repeated over and over after it has gotten a laugh. Repetition means safety, ritual, familiarity. It can also mean boredom.

Pete and Repeat were walking down the street.
Pete fell down.

Who was left?

Repeat.

Pete and Repeat were walking down the street.
Pete fell down.

Who was left?

Repeat.

Pete and Repeat....

Repetition as pathology is a very different matter. In language it is known as perseveration; in actions, stereotypy; in thoughts, obsession. Those hiccups were benign, but some of J.P.'s later "repetitions" were far from it. To look at a list of fragile X behaviors is to see the prefix "hyper" attached to many otherwise neutral words: *hyper*-activity, *hyper*-sensitivity, *hyper*-vigilance, *hyper*-arousal. *Hyper*, meaning *over, above, beyond*—reactions out of proportion to the stimulus. In fragile X, there is too much: too much of a stretch of DNA, too much sensitivity to the world, too much activity, too much fear, the body surging with too much adrenaline. It is a mutation of excess, leading to behaviors that go beyond what society finds acceptable. Like Mardi Gras all year long: wild dancing and flung beads, sudden nudity and acts of deviance. The life of a family with a child with fragile X (or heaven help us, two or three children with fragile X) is a site of public gawking and extreme exhaustion. It is more than you bargained for.

Let's start with hyperactivity, an overused category since sometime in the 1980s, with seemingly every other child, especially boys, being labeled in this way. With only slight exaggeration, I thought the word had been invented for J.P. From the time J.P. could walk (late, at 19 months), he was in constant movement. The first reports from his early intervention program rang changes on this theme. "He is often in constant motion within the room"; his teachers note a "lack of purposeful movement...demonstrated by his running ability which he does well but does so when agitated or excited, not when encouraged by other children or in the context of a game." "J.P. will work at tabletop activities for three minutes with constant prompts ....The only activities he will pursue longer are those of a non-adaptive, repetitive, and perseverative nature, e.g., toy dashboard with horn, flashing lights and squeals." (Life in our household in those days was noisy.) "With

54

regard to sensory integration, J. P. has demonstrated difficulties with this area during class by his excessive desire for vestibular stimulation (swinging) and his continual movement even during tabletop activities."

The occupational therapist suggested that we try techniques called joint compression and brushing. Lay the child on the floor (flailing and giddy as usual), and methodically push his forearms into the elbow joint, then push his lower legs into the knee socket. Using a soft therapeutic brush that looks like a lint cleaner, brush the child's arms and legs vigorously as he giggles and writhes. Repeat six to seven times a day. After three weeks of this routine, J.P. was no less hyperactive than he had ever been.

J.P., like most children with fragile X syndrome (and those with autism), has problems with sensory processing. Many of his dysfunctional behaviors are the result of his hypersensitivity to sights, sounds, touch, taste, and smell. When the outside world overwhelms him, he turns to self-stimulation, repetitive behaviors that soothe and ground him. Fragile X kids are known for flapping their hands not just at moments of excitement, but whenever the world around them is too much. J.P. also spins, a successor to the swinging he enjoyed as a toddler. He turns around and around in a circle well past the point when a typical person would be reeling with dizziness, his face in a state of bliss, my domestic whirling dervish. When he stops, his eyes still spin like a cartoon character that has been hit in the head. I've learned simply to witness this ritual and not to interfere with what is as soothing to him as saying the Rosary is to my mother.

Plagued with low muscle tone and faulty proprioception, the so-called sixth sense that lets a person locate his body in space, J.P. knows instinctively how to get the sensory input he needs. When he was 4 or 5 years old, he would go to the walk-in closet in our master bedroom and pile his father's clothes on top of his body. He also liked my husband, Harry, to place a 4-foot long, sausage-shaped pillow, a gold velour relic from the 1970s, on top of his body and playfully squash him. Only later, when we were advised to try deep pressure to calm him, did we realize that J.P. had concocted his own therapy before we could do it for him. Using an established therapy, J.P.'s preschool teacher, Pat Borges, generously sewed a denim vest for him that looked like a photographer's vest, except that weights were placed in the multiple pockets instead of lenses. Although it hurt me to see my 4-year-old bearing an extra 8 pounds on his 42-pound frame, J.P. didn't seem to mind wearing the vest. Some mornings, Pat told me, he would even ask to wear it, seeking the grounded feeling that it must have given his wildly flying little body.

Other repetitive movements have not been as benign as spinning or flapping. For years J.P. has shredded paper—book pages, flyers, scrap paper, newspapers, and magazines—hiding piles of the stuff behind the couch, carting out bags surreptitiously to the trash can. "Why?" I implore him over and over. As he has gotten older, he replies plaintively, "My hands...my hands," holding them up helplessly. The nervous energy pouring through his body seems to pool there, where he feels their agitation as an alien force, like two frantic squirrels digging in the leaves outside your window. There is no premeditation in his ripping, nothing but pure mechanical release.

From infancy almost up to the present, J.P. has chewed on whatever was nearby: shirt collars and cuffs, toys, books, paper, the arms of the sofa. When he was 9 years old, his chewing almost turned deadly when he chewed up a medicinal patch affixed to his back. The patch contained clonidine, a drug usually used for high blood pressure but that he takes even today to calm his over-aroused system. J.P. and I were spending the Christmas holidays with my parents in St. Louis, where I had grown up, when he came upstairs from the basement where he had been watching videos. I was on the phone with a high school friend making plans for an informal reunion that night. As I talked, I idly ran my hand over my son's back and with a jolt realized that the patch was not there. I asked him about it, and though he looked guilt-stricken, he could not or would not admit to removing it. I had a sudden inspiration: I asked J.P. to open his mouth and I inserted my finger, only to pull out small shreds of patch, wet and papery. He had no doubt chewed the patch like you'd chew a stick of gum while he ran and reran his favorite video.

I didn't panic, not believing this benign drug could cause any damage. My mother, however, suggested that I call the local Poison Control Center. When I explained the situation to the operator, she said, slowly and deliberately, as if talking to a child, "Now, get your son and take him to the nearest emergency room." "The hospital?" I said stupidly. "Don't waste any time," came the syrupy voice. "He needs medical attention *now*." I bundled J.P. into his jacket and the three of us scurried into the car; I cradled J.P. in the back seat, while my mom drove to the hospital. I was still not very worried because he seemed normally alert, but by the time we arrived at the emergency room, he was quiet and sleepy-looking.

Nonetheless, J.P. roused himself when the nurses tried to attach him to a monitor. Kicking and lunging, he fought with all the excess adrenaline that still surged in his body. Mom and I watched helplessly as eventually J.P. had to be pinned down by two large orderlies so he could be hooked up to all the equipment needed to assess his vital signs. The patch he had chewed was relatively new, and carried almost 25 days' worth of clonidine. Now the drug was steadily pushing his blood pressure down to dangerous levels.

"Could he die?" I asked, not for a moment believing in the unthinkable. "It's unlikely," the doctor said carefully, "but untreated, this kind of overdose could result in death. The chief danger is that he will fall into a coma." Soon J.P. fell asleep and was moved to a hospital room where I spent the night with him, waiting and watching for his blood pressure to rise and stabilize. I sat next to his bed and later lay sleepless on a cot, the glow of the splint he wore on his finger a beacon for me in the dark limbo of the night. Nurses came and went at 2, at 3, at 4 a.m., raising the bed, checking monitors, asking my semiconscious boy to urinate in a bottle. Finally morning came, and J.P. began to wake up, crying a little and gazing wildly around the unfamiliar hospital room. I cried a little myself, in exhaustion and relief.

As the day wore on, J.P. became vivacious, even giddy, thrilled to have his mom's full attention for hours. My parents and siblings visited his room, bringing a McDonald's Happy Meal. He was enjoying it all so much I feared he would try this again someday. When he was released from the bed, he lurched down the hall, still woozy with clonidine, but rattling off crazy phrases and moving nonstop. A call to his doctor back in Boston informed me that he was having a rebound effect to the overdose; once sedated to the point of unconsciousness, he was now literally bouncing off the walls of the hospital. It seemed there could be no equilibrium for my unbalanced little boy.

I was on an emotional roller coaster during those days, too. It was only the second Christmas since my divorce had become final in December of 1993. With some bitterness, I spoke to Harry's secretary back in Boston to try to reach him with news of J.P.'s accident. Harry was on a skiing vacation with his new girlfriend, and I can't say that I didn't take some shameful pleasure in interrupting it with my news. By the time I reached him, J.P. was rapidly recovering, so Harry never felt the terror I had felt the night before. As usual, his response didn't satisfy me, and I hung up the phone feeling the burden of parenthood— at least for the moment—to be entirely my own.

This was also only the second Christmas after my extended family had received the diagnosis of fragile X. I don't remember any discussion, either then or earlier, about what had befallen our family: four of my parents' five children carrying the premutation, and four of their then five grandchildren cursed with full-blown fragile X. Though J.P.'s diagnosis had pulled my siblings, their children, and my parents together into a dragnet of grief, when we were in each other's company, we all stepped delicately over the net. Yet I couldn't help noticing the profusion of presents my parents gave us that year. As kids we had always received heaps of presents, more than the average, but this year.... A washer and dryer for my youngest sister and her husband, furniture for another sister's family, suit jackets and cashmere sweaters for the brothers-in-law, rocking horses and expensive American Girl dolls. The loot kept coming. At day's end, we sat stunned among the mounds of wrapping paper, rolling in a guilty bounty, drowning in unspoken sorrow.

From J.P.'s lair in the basement of the house he and I share, the same six or eight bars of music blast out over and over and over: "Tell me why-yi-yi-yi." It's always the first song, always the first line, no chance to progress to other notes and words. As we drive in the car and play a CD, J.P. says urgently, "Number one, number one." "But we've heard it three times," I protest. "Again, again," he says, as I know he will. (His reiterations lead to my reiterations—futile, Pavlovian responses that belie my higher IQ.) From the living room comes the sound of the scene in the movie *Home Alone* where Kevin, played by Macaulay Culkin, looks at himself in the mirror while shaving and screams, wide-eyed as Munch's famous painting, "Ahhhhhhhh." Pause. "Ahhhhhhhh." Pause. "Ahhhhhhhh." I learn to tune it out, but occasionally it breaks through and then—you guessed it—it's me screaming, "Ahhhhhhhh. Turn that off!"

The constant replaying of one part of the tape, whether audio or video, eventually wears it out, but sometimes it doesn't last that long. Turning the tape over and over in his hands, J.P. eventually pulls the plastic ribbon out of its case. A more potent fetish is the music CD. When J.P. catches sight of one, his whole body quivers in anticipation. With the urgency of a drug addict, he rips off the impossible shrink wrap faster than anyone else could, and breathes heavily over the disc. "Isn't it gorgeous?" he asks. Soon he is spinning it relentlessly and deftly in his hands, like the machine the disk is meant for, his eyes mesmerized as if he were spinning himself. I think the CD would survive him if he stopped there. But inevitably, whether in 5 minutes or in an hour, he will bite the shining disk or break it with the very intensity of his lust.

It is like living with an alcoholic. I can't leave a CD lying around the house and I have to lock up my own CDs. Scores of CDs that I've had through the years are lost to me, or will skip annoyingly at just about the ninth song. (Did you ever notice that the old LPs repeated a phrase when they skipped, but scratched CDs just jump? At least I am spared more repetition.) I can't buy CDs for J.P. even though he loves music more than anything else, and it's difficult to find tapes these days. Since J.P. has so few interests, it saddens me to deprive him of the objects he loves, but there is a limit to the amount of destruction I can tolerate.

As it is, the finished basement of our house has been laid waste by J.P.'s ripping and breaking, but also by his habit of scribbling on whatever he can reach, including the painted, paneled walls. When we moved into the house, the basement was a pristine almond color, with a thick white Berber carpet, built-in bookshelves, and stereo compartments with glass doors. Now the carpet is stained, and the glass doors have broken off. The door leading to the garage proclaims "Mom," like a sailor's tattoo. The wall at the base of the stairs shouts "Roise" (J.P.'s favored spelling for Rosie O'Donnell, one of his obsessions till her show went off the air). "Pooh" is inscribed on the wall over the sofa; check marks line the panels of the doors that house the electric meter; the names or initials of his classmates—S.B., Ben, Tina—crop up at regular intervals on all the walls.

The basement has become the dark and hidden underbelly of the house and bears the stigma of my incapacity as a mother. I feel shame as I pass through it to the laundry room or the garage, shame when I have to let a workman into it, shame when my ex-husband sees it. Once the first inroads were made about nine years ago, I made a strategic decision to let J.P.'s destructiveness run its course before redecorating. "Wait till you're sure he won't do it again," my mother urges whenever I'm tempted to redecorate. J.P. is now 20 and at last look, one of the graffiti betrays its recent inscription: "Tina," a girl whose name he has only been writing compulsively in the past year, when they worked together in a supervised job as part of his program. It is not yet safe to wipe out the past. It is not yet safe to pretend we are a normal family. No sense pretending I can control my son's compulsions.

Your child may enjoy the story of Snow White. My child, between the ages of 4 and 6, lived, breathed, and consumed Snow White. We went through a dozen copies of the storybook as J.P. ripped them up in excitement. He manhandled the Seven Dwarfs in squeeze-toy form, mouthing them hungrily throughout the day. We played the taped story over and over and over. When J.P. was 8 it happened again with Tomie de Paola's children's book, *Strega Nona*, the story of an Italian "grandmother witch" who has magic powers. J.P. injected Strega Nona into every aspect of his daily life until his doctor suggested that he might not know the difference between fantasy and reality. I never believed this, that he had a psychosis, as she put it; rather, he chose to dwell in a story that resonated for him in some vital way, to remain in its grandmotherly embrace, avoiding a world that demanded the processing of new stimuli. Strega made life a theme park. She domesticated a wild world of terrifying sensations.

Today, at 20, J.P. is obsessed with Oprah Winfrey, though "obsessed" is not a word strong enough to describe his relentless discussion of her daily show, her hair—he calls it "mopsy" and rarely approves of it—her garb on the cover of her magazine (of course he has a subscription), her sayings ("Keep it simple," he intones as he leaves the house for school). He e-mails me from school, simply: "Oprah best show." He checks her Web site regularly to see what topics she will discuss that week. The Oprah-fication of J.P.'s life is comical, annoying, banal, intriguing, and finally, transparent. The function Oprah serves, like her sisters Snow White and Strega Nona, is to simplify J.P.'s life, her motto ironically explaining why my son loves her. For his world— our world—is so decidedly *not* simple. At the physical level, it is noisy, bright, odorous, abrasive, or eerily slick. You can't count on much: different people in your life make different demands on you, have different standards (mom, dad, teachers, bus driver, the man behind the checkout counter). The day's schedule changes, too, as people change their minds, it snows, the car breaks down. (Gee, I wish I had an Oprah.)

But Oprah appears every day, at 4 p.m. on the dot, and the afternoon falls into place. There is before-Oprah and after-Oprah, and in some sense that matters as much as during-Oprah, maybe even more. For J.P. is rarely in the moment; his favorite question is "And then what?" This is usually repeated—yes, repeated—after every answer you can give him. It's as if time is a yawning abyss and what keeps him from falling in is the scaffold of schedule. He keeps—we keep—daily schedules. Here is a sample from his journal, kept in a composition notebook, one of which he goes through in about two days. (Why? Because he writes some things over and over.)

> Thursday, February 5, 2004
>
> Bear 6:30
>
> eat food mom
>
> go WHS
>
> Ms. Dacey
>
> Oprah

It ends there, though on other days he will write "6:30 mom," to note my homecoming. Bracketed by two TV shows and their characters—The Bear in the Big Blue House and Oprah—and pinned on two of his favorite people in between, his teacher Ms. Dacey and his mom, the bulk of his day at WHS (Wayland High School) is not deconstructed here. The next page, however, lists the periods of the high school day:

> Math
>
> English
>
> Currt E [Current Events]
>
> Lunch
>
> work

And so it goes, day after day. The schedule may not change much, but *it will be set down*. Intrusions like "hair cut, 5 p.m.," are tolerated but unsettling. And God forbid if Oprah is preempted for a national disaster or a local ceremony. The firm scaffold of the afternoon gives way, and anything could happen. And then what?

I'll tell you what. J.P. may erupt in a disordered language that his father calls "ragtime." He begins to call me "Shannon," his classmate and "girlfriend." He says he hates "Chas," his classmate who rides the bus with him. He begins to rip up his latest Oprah magazine. He retreats to the basement to sing loudly and obnoxiously. He knows I'm not Shannon and he doesn't hate Chas, but at this moment his feelings are out of control and logic is set aside.

"Outbursts," the psychologists call them, or "meltdowns"—the times when sensory input or anxiety overwhelms the person with fragile X. "Down" and "out," the directions of failure and ostracism, experiences all too common to my son and others like him. And let it be said: of their families, too. If I am to describe J.P.'s behavior with understanding and compassion, I also have to own up to the intense feelings of frustration and shame—even rage—that come with the job of being his mother.

When J.P. was younger, his outbursts were more catastrophic, and he could fall to the ground, kicking and screaming, often biting his hand or biting me. Something as mundane as singing "Happy Birthday" at his birthday party would set him off. To this day he begs us not to observe this ritual: "No singing!" he warns us, and we know that means no blowing out candles either.

When J.P. began to use language to express himself, even primitively, things improved slightly. But language can be hurled as a weapon, too, and words like "fuckface" and "asshole" sometimes made me wish for inarticulate shrieks. The years J.P. was in fifth and sixth grades, his outbursts became more frequent and more alarming. The literature that I had read on fragile X mentioned increased aggressiveness around puberty, something you can't imagine when your boy is little and giggly, no matter how hyper. Even small boys with fragile X will hit impulsively when they are overwhelmed, but when they grow larger and testosterone floods their bodies, a violent outburst has more serious consequences. J.P. is by nature affectionate and joking, and everything he did even in this period of his life could be matched by other, more composed moments. But I can't deny that at that stage, as he lashed out at the world, I often felt a despair I had never imagined even when we received his diagnosis. At times we both spiraled out of control.

The worst part of the day was without doubt the transitional hour in the morning between home and school. A typical day when J.P. was in middle school began like this: Long before the alarm sounds at 6:30 a.m., I awaken to the sound of J.P. screeching or shouting song lyrics on the floor below me. He has been up since 5 or 5:30 and the previous night's medications have worn off. He is hyper and ravenous. No warnings I have given him the day before (and the day before that) will withstand the force of his raw energy, the crossed wires of his nervous system. I cringe under the covers, dreading what I will meet downstairs. Sure enough, I find a heap of shredded papers in the front hallway, a hunk of meatloaf in the living room, smears of peanut butter on the kitchen counter. If I dared look, I would find far worse behind the couch in the basement, where J.P. is watching cartoons. But I don't go there.

I call J.P. and begin to get him dressed for school. He is 11, but he still puts on his shirts backwards and cannot button his pants. He gives me a hug, anything not to focus on the task at hand, getting dressed for school. "That's inside out, come here," I say coaxingly. He is laughing helplessly and hysterically, falling to the ground and refusing to cooperate. He keeps laughing, and now he is repeating a word that he has heard—"halibut"—because it has struck some obscure funny bone in his body. He won't let go of it: "halibut," "halibut," "halibut." He grabs the bowl of yogurt I set out and eats it hungrily, smearing some on his clean shirt. I try to remind him to show his teacher his daily notebook, as I have written her a note there. His eyes are looking at the TV and his hands are covered in yogurt. "Come wash your hands. No, with soap. Please, dry them! No, come back. You've got to take your pills. All right. Here is your lunch money. Be careful, put it in the knapsack!" "Halibut, halibut! I love you, Mommy! I hate you, Mommy!"

Now we approach the front door. My stomach tenses. This has become the climax of the morning madness. J.P. must walk down the path from our house, on a slight hill, to the street where the school van is waiting. He jostles me roughly as he pushes toward the front door.

"Damn you," he shouts and then he turns around and spits on the front door. I can't stop myself, I yell back at him, "Stop that! Get on that bus!" He runs down to the curb, past the bus, and into the street. He looks up at the house, daring me to intervene. When he sees me start out of the house in my bathrobe, he scurries to the side of the van and hops in. When the van takes off, I shiver in relief. My body only relaxes when I see it turn the corner of our street.

One of these jagged mornings, on the ride to school, J.P. threw a book the length of his van and hit the bus driver in the head. Luckily the driver wasn't hurt nor did he lose control of the van. After this incident, though the town did not ban us from the transportation J.P. was entitled to by law, I thought that for the safety of all concerned, I should drive J.P. to school every day. Though he entered my car more readily than the bus in the mornings, he still fell to pieces when he arrived at the school. He spat on my car, screamed "I hate you" at me, and stood stock still on the playground, yelling insults at passing students ("asshole," "jerk," "idiot"). I watched other mothers drop off their children, give a jaunty wave and drive off, and there I would be, trying to get my son to let go of the car door so I wouldn't run him over.

One morning in sixth grade, when he was still taking the bus, I watched J.P. gear up for the usual frenzy that preceded his entering the outside world. Suddenly, without warning, J.P. pulled back his arm and punched me in the eye. We were about the same height and by then he outweighed me. Stunned and angry, I somehow pushed him out the door and with shouts and curses, he eventually did get into the van. I shut the front door, leaned against it, and sliding slowly down to the floor, sobbed uncontrollably. My natural instinct to survive, to fight back when attacked, banged up against a mother's instinct to withstand anything her child might do. I knew all the clinical reasons why J.P. had hit me, but I also knew, in a fierce and visceral flash, that I would not allow myself to be battered. I felt suspended in that moment between a fear that felt like anger, a rush of adrenaline that was just as strong as J.P.'s, and something just as powerful: my fierce love for my son. Though he only hit me a couple of more times, I made some calls that year to get the names of possible residential schools should I reach my limits. It felt like a back-up plan that you never hope to use. I didn't know if I would be able to let him go, but I didn't know if I would be able to let him stay.

Fifteen years before, when Harry and I had only been married a year, we decided to get a cat. I chose a kitten from an animal shelter and brought it home to our shabby apartment in Brookline. We bandied names around—Luna, Moony, Scooter (for some reason they all had a pouting, cooing sound)—but for some reason never settled on one. We kept the kitten at night in a room we called the Tundra, a former screened porch that the landlord had converted to year-round use with cheap paneling and a gold shag carpet. The wind blew around the edges of the windows in the Tundra, and the New England cold penetrated its thin walls. The kitten may have had her reasons, but she would not use the litterbox we set out. She began to urinate on the shag carpet and in other spots in the apartment. If the mother cat hadn't trained her, my own mother warned me, our kitten would now never take to the box. The smell from the shag carpet became unbearable and I knew I had to return her to the shelter. I also knew what the shelter would do with such a cat.

As I walked down Beacon Street towards the trolley, carrying a box with the kitten in my arms, I began to cry. I had taken on this responsibility and now I was reneging, sending this innocent little creature to certain death. I had never had a pet before—I didn't even have many plants—and I had been an impatient older sister. I sometimes wondered what kind of mother I would be. I felt that someone else might have been able to train the cat, and make a home for her, but it seemed I was not that woman.

Not long before this episode I had talked on the phone to a high school friend who had married some years before me and already had three children. Nancy was a lot like me: high-strung, exuberant, yet serious at heart, a good Catholic girl. She told me that one day, in a rare moment alone in the car, and feeling overwhelmed with the burden of her life as a mother, she had had a sudden urge simply to keep on driving. She would move on, shaking off her three little girls like snowflakes. Of course she hadn't done it, but I sensed the despair in her voice and it haunted me in those first months of marriage. What was I capable of when it came to never-ending care?

Every night, every night, night 342
And counting, my son asks fast
And sharp as I tuck him in,
"Anystorms? Anyblackouts?"
Checks on the list of fears
That flood his body

I'm the boat
In the rising tide
I'm the lighthouse
In the closing dark
Lord give me the strength
To rise above these seas

Sometimes when I'm really tired,
On edge, self-pitying single
Mother, I don't let him ask
(nails on a blackboard)
I seize the day and back out the door
Chanting "nostormsnoblackouts"
On my way

Nostormsnoblackouts

What am I promising?

Lightning could strike me

For my lies

But he's satisfied...

For the moment...

Until night 343....

For a homework assignment when he was 15, J.P. was asked to make a list of the times when he felt brave and when he felt afraid. The assignment was not difficult for a boy whose genetic inheritance had cursed him with an almost constant anxiety. Under the heading "Brave" he listed "having Mom around, singing, taking a deep breath, and 'emptying my cup,'" a metaphor the kids had learned in school to induce calm. Under the heading "Afraid," J.P. listed "lightning, storms, blackouts, thunder, wind, doctor visits, and the dentist." It was a major accomplishment for J.P. to be able to articulate these fears, and it gave me a look into J.P.'s world, a place of daily disasters lightened by love and trust.

If I felt weary promising night after night that there would be no blackouts, it had been far more draining to fend off J.P. as a toddler, when he could not give words to his fears. When he was 6, he went through a period, as many kids do, of resisting bedtime, but he seemed to get stuck in a loop that I could not enter. It was the summer his father and I had separated, and J.P. and I were living alone in our sprawling, five-bedroom house. Desperate at night to have respite from my hyperactive little boy and to give in to my grief, I would put him to bed and shut his bedroom door with an almost physical urge for breathing space. He must have sensed my need, because within minutes he would be out of the room and at the door of my own bedroom, where I had taken refuge.

I would lead him back to bed. He would return. "Pleeeease go to bed," I begged. I would lead him back. He would return. Finally, after a dozen trips back and forth, I held his door shut, almost hysterical with the need to regroup. He would scream and hold the other knob, then throw himself at the door. The return of the repressed, I called it to myself, but it was no laughing matter. At times like these it was all I could do to restrain myself from hurting my son: I was stretched so thin myself, that I did not have the resources to stay calm as I was bombarded—like he was, I guess—by that which I could not control.

When I was a little girl I had a recurring nightmare, though it is better called a waking dream, never truly lived in sleep. I deliberately terrified myself by trying to imagine eternity, a concept that was a regular part of my instruction in Catholic school. Heaven was eternal, hell was eternal, and purgatory was only a way station. Life after death had no end. All that I knew of life—humid summer afternoons yielding to crisp fall mornings, second grade following first, the diary page turning over to a new day—would be lost in the next life. I didn't really see myself going to hell; my sins were more venial than mortal. But I desperately did not want to go to heaven if it meant an uninflected bliss. Huddled in my bed at night I stretched my mind to try to envision endlessness—and it balked. I repeated to myself over and over, "day after day after day after day after day" until I couldn't take it anymore. I needed markers; I needed highs and lows; I needed punctuation. Sheesh. I didn't know how God did it. And that was just time; space, too, was endless in heaven. Infinity was just as unthinkable as eternity.

The natural horror I felt in contemplating the endless and the shapeless as a child had an uncanny resonance in the thinking of Gerard Manley Hopkins, my dissertation subject many years later when I was a graduate student in English. Hopkins was haunted by a Darwinian vision of man reduced to insignificance in a world rolling endlessly into eternity:

> *Manshape, that shone*
>
> *Sheer off, disseveral, a star, death blots black out; nor mark*
>
> *Is any of him at all so stark*
>
> *But vastness blurs and time beats level.*

Hopkins invented the notion of "inscape" out of his desire to assert the "especial" nature of an individual form, whether natural or human, the principle of its uniqueness. I share Hopkins's deeply felt need to rescue life from its own amorphousness. I write about my son's behavior to catch the inscape of fragile X, to seize the singular from a mass of repetition and somehow craft a shape that is as inevitable as DNA. I want one where there is many, less where there is more, a clean line where there is a blur. I want to hear the second song on the CD, and the third, and all of them, including the last.

The story of Strega Nona, J.P.'s passing obsession as a child, reaches its climax when the witless Big Anthony, a kind of slow learner himself, is left with a magic pot that makes unlimited amounts of pasta, and tries to use it without knowing the spell that makes the pot stop. Pasta is rolling down the streets of Calabria, the town is being inundated, and Big Anthony is in a panic. Pasta is the stuff of life, but you can always have too much of a good thing. Only Strega Nona has the knowledge to stop the pot's mindless flood. She returns in the knick of time, blows three kisses, and the pasta stops. A triplet of love, and everything returns to normal. Ah. If only.

Here We Go Again

Tracey Anderson lives in Colorado Springs with her two
awesome boys, one of whom has fragile X.

It's early, but my eyes open to welcome in the sun. I rise and slowly
make my way down the stairs to the beckoning aroma of the freshly
brewed coffee. Here we go again. I wonder if I can muster the strength
to get through another day. Yes, of course I can, because as my 3-year-
old says, he has the brains, Kellen has the heart, and I have the courage.
The morning is beautiful and so quiet the rest of the world seems to
have ceased to exist, if only for a brief moment in time. I walk out onto
the patio with my second cup of coffee to breathe…just breathe.

From inside the house, I hear the familiar. "Mom…oooo
whooo…way aw ewe?" It's my 5 1/2-year-old son Kellen. Beautiful,
blue-eyed, blond, sweet, loving, passionate Kellen, who also happens
to have fragile X syndrome. I feel a sudden rush of mixed emotions
immediately overcome me: the pure joy of seeing and being with my
son and the wave of exhaustion just from anticipating what lies in
store for the day. I waited so many years to hear him utter the word
"mom" that I always feel guilty wishing for just a few more moments
of nothingness. Here we go again. The silent and tranquil entry into the

new day will soon deviate into quite a different scenario. Kellen's little brother Dorian (who does not have fragile X) is still asleep as Kellen proceeds to track me down in my temporary state of peace.

The sounds of the morning—birds, the occasional car in the distance, the slow production of ice cubes in the ice maker, and the almost constant refilling of the leaky toilet tank—will exist no more, drowned out by the squeals and screams of my two sons. Kellen can reach the high notes, the ones that cause temporary blindness. The notes that should break glass. The notes that pierce through every nerve synapse in my body, simulating electric shock. How many times will I make the futile effort to shush him during this day? "Kellen…ssshhhh!" followed by placing a finger to my lips. "Okay, mom," spoken so compliantly yet attached seamlessly and concurrently to yet another squeal that should only be audible to dogs, but yet echoes through the house and most likely the neighborhood as well. I'm lucky that I have good neighbors. They tolerate the volume from our little corner of the world. They know us and they love Kellen.

It's the people who don't know why he screams and tantrums like he does that cause us even more strife extending beyond our daily tribulations. Like the time when we were at the park and Kellen was in inconsolable meltdown mode. Someone called the police. That was before we had Kellen's diagnosis. Imagine the surprise of seeing two police cruisers pull up and both of the uniformed officers proceed directly to us! It has become mandatory for my sanity to find the humor in these situations, even if it comes several weeks later. That year Kellen dressed as a convict for Halloween. Although he couldn't tolerate the activity of trick-or-treating, he looked cute and it allowed for an amusing memory.

It's my day off from work, and I want to spend it with my boys. What should we do today? While routine is an integral part of Kellen's life, it is amazingly difficult to plan a day. What will entertain them both? What can we do that won't overstimulate Kellen too soon and cut the fun short for Dorian? Our outings are dictated by Kellen's ability to deal with the situation. Maybe we'll go to the park. Maybe he can play for an hour. Maybe for five minutes. However long it takes, soon the meltdown will start its reign over our adventure. I will tell Dorian, "We have to go now. Kellen is having a hard time." Dorian will want to stay and not understand why we always have to go when Kellen wants to. Is that fair to Dorian? No. Is fragile X fair to Kellen? No.

Ah, the conveniences of the modern world. The all-important television—it can bring a welcome break to our afternoon. Well, a break in the sense that I can be in a different room for a moment. But the break is only partial as the screeches and screams produced by Kellen over the favorite scenes of the show still make me feel as though I am running a marathon. "Kellen…ssshhhh!"

It's amazing how many pertinent applications can be derived from all those cartoons we seem to watch endlessly. Like every other parent today, I know a good portion of them verbatim. One of them will always remain close to my heart: "….Our family is small and broken, but still good, yes good." It's not accurate to insinuate that we need fixing. We don't. We just need to live, learn, and adapt, which we will continue to do for the rest of our lives.

It's dark now. The sounds of the day have once again calmed into an eerie ringing in my ears. The boys are asleep accompanied by their deep, repetitive breathing and sweaty little foreheads. The dog is asleep. The cat is asleep. The birds are asleep. The neighbors are asleep. I should be asleep, but I just stand in the kitchen and alternate looking into the different rooms of my temporarily still and quiet home. What do I have left to do tonight? What did I forget to do today? What do I need to remember for tomorrow? I can't think anymore today. I slowly make my way back up the stairs to the engulfing comfort of my bed and close my eyes. Here we go again.

Plan B

Barry Berg is a writer and a teacher who has a son with fragile X syndrome.

The first thing you should know is that I was 53 years old when my son Julian was born. Clearly, I did not enter fatherhood or, for that matter, my marriage to Susan in a carefree manner. I had always taken my life seriously, trying to think through all important decisions. Of course, I knew decisions of marriage and parenthood are not ones that yield to easy analysis; possibly they yielded to no analysis at all. Perhaps they were leaps of faith. Nevertheless, I had a brain; I tried to use it.

From earliest childhood I valued my independence, and growing into adulthood I was happy to finally be free. My time was my own. I was no longer accountable to parents or schools. I chose the profession of writer, in part, because it fitted those needs. I had no office to report to, and of course, no boss. In every way possible, I wanted to "own" myself, and I luxuriated in that freedom. Yes, I did get married. Twice. But in both marriages I looked for women who I not only loved and respected, but who also had a quality of self that did not depend upon me for completion. In both cases I succeeded. When I met Susan I was impressed that she loved me, and at the same time understood that I could not define myself solely as half of a pair. Please do not misread. Being a couple is critical to a marriage. I understand that, and I value commitment and responsibility as much as I value independence.

But having a child is something else. Watching friends raise their families, I could see that parenthood meant you don't own very much of your self anymore. Also, you can pretty much choose your spouse, but unless you adopt a teenager you don't get to choose your child. You don't know if it will be a boy or a girl. You don't know if it will be good-looking or odd. You don't know if it will be athletic or musical or even nice. I have seen perfectly pleasant people bring children into this world who were just plain unlikable. Okay, scratch unlikable. Let's call them "difficult." I have seen children emerge from the womb fretting, whining, even screaming, and some never stop. Please—I don't blame the children. There are chemical and environmental factors that go into who we are and how we behave that we may never understand. But I don't blame the parents, either. When I was young, and a better liberal than I am today, I thought that children turned out one way or another because of how parents treated them. But even before I had Julian, I could see this was not always true. A toxic parent or an abusive environment will destroy a child; I have seen more than enough evidence of that. But some children survive even the worst beginnings and do well in life. And others, for no obvious reason, enter this world screaming.

What if I had one of those? What if I had a child I did not like? The thought sent a shudder down my spine. What if I had a child who did not love me? It was possible. For a man who, in equal measure, wanted control over his life and needed to be loved, this was not a pleasant contemplation.

And beneath these concerns, the thought I could not utter aloud because it was woven too deeply into my core, and with too binding a force: what if I had a child who was damaged? I was not confident how much I would love this child. And in such a case, no matter what, the life I had planned would be gone. It was this unbidden and unexpressed dread as much as any spoken reason—what sort of person would say it aloud?— that kept me from parenthood those first 50 years.

But somehow I had changed. Somehow, this time, I was agreeing not only to a marriage, but to having a child. There was only one way that a man with my set of concerns, and my educational background, could deal with the inevitable near future.

Denial.

Let me explain denial as I understand it, and as I do you will gather it is a psychological structure near and dear to my heart.

Denial exists on many levels. Infants and young children employ it as a powerful and necessary defense. If some idea or piece of knowledge is too painful or too anxiety-provoking, it simply does not exist. Susan and I are in the car with Julian, who is 5 years old and still drinking from a bottle. He has finished his milk and wants more. Susan tells him we don't have more milk, he must wait until we get home. Her words are too distressful, so he denies them. "Yes, you do have milk," he wails. "You do, you do!" Tell a 3-year-old that Grandpa has died, that we will never see him again, and that child may well argue with you and say it could not be true. It is too painful a concept to take in, so the young mind rightfully denies it for a period of time, until the awful fact can be digested.

But denial is not just for the very young. Along with its cousin, rationalization, it serves us all. I might argue that religions—which tell us with no evidence but only faith that we will see Grandpa again in Paradise—are finding a comfortable and constructive use of denial. I might argue that, but I won't. At least not here. Let me focus instead on my own deadly playful use of this defense, through the birth of my son.

To start, I never believed I would become a parent. Yes, I had learned on the streets of Brooklyn how babies were made. And yes, I knew I was currently involved in risky behavior. But neither Susan nor I were young. I was probably sterile. No, I had no reason to believe that, but I might just as well be as not. Susan is a DES daughter. Her mother had taken that drug during her own pregnancy, which meant Susan might find it harder to conceive and was possibly more likely to miscarry. And the chance that one sperm would swim up to wherever it swims up to and find an egg to fertilize—I mean, what were the odds of that happening? No, no, no, Susan may want to get pregnant, but really, I was safe. Wasn't I?

Then one day her period was late. Well, that had happened before. And then she took one of those home pregnancy tests, but how reliable is that? Besides, the color of the little stick that was supposed to turn purple if she was pregnant, well, it might be a shade of blue, okay, reddish-blue, but surely that wasn't purple. Then she went to a doctor and a test I could not argue with told us she was, indeed, undeniably, oh-so-pregnant.

Okay. It was a blow. I had lost a battle. But I would not lose this war. My denial had to retreat to a more defensible line. Now I would admit Susan was pregnant. In fact we did all the things couples do when they are expecting a child. Susan watched her diet. We attended Lamaze classes. We acquired a crib. We had sonograms. We did all these things while—please believe this—I never allowed myself to think that at the end of this pregnancy there would be a baby. We did all the things couples do when they are expecting a child, except the father was never actually expecting one.

Understand that this was a trick of mind. I am not psychotic, and if someone asked I would have said, "Of course we are having a baby in May." But the defense allowed this knowledge to skate along on some surface of my mind; it never truly entered. Deep inside I felt I was saying that because it would be crazy not to. But it wasn't really going to happen. So as you might imagine, it was a rude shock when early on a Saturday morning in April, not May, Susan came out of the bathroom with a perplexed look on her face. She wasn't sure what had just happened, but she might have broken her water.

Hmm. What to do? I agreed we should probably take her to the hospital. I mean, something was going on, and I wasn't going to handle it at home. I gave the matter particularly sober thought because Susan was scheduled to have her baby shower the next day, and I didn't want her to miss that. So—okay. It was still early in the day. We'd go to the hospital and have the doctor look at her. No need to pack a bag. We'd be home for dinner.

You are well ahead of me, dear reader. Had this been reality TV, there would have been no adult in the western world not ahead of me. Of course the doctor confirmed that Susan had indeed broken her water, and she was going to give birth this weekend. But this is the lesson here: Never underestimate the flexibility and strength of denial. I remember thinking at this precise moment—Saturday morning at 11:00—that if we induced labor quickly she could have the …well, you know…she could have "it," get cleaned up, rest a little, and still attend her shower tomorrow morning. Yes. That is exactly what I thought. If you haven't already noticed, denial easily passes for stupidity.

I remember dealing with the labor quite well. Susan was in some discomfort, then in some pain. And then quite a lot of pain. I got her ice to chew on, and I monitored the drugs. At 4 in the morning I found a second doctor when she needed an epidural. This was not a problem for me. This woman I loved was in pain and undergoing a medical procedure, and of course I was helping the best I could. What did that have to do with a baby?

Finally at 7:20 a.m. it was over. I saw the doctor take this…well, I didn't know what to think or even what to call it, but it was long and thin and extremely odd shaped, not easy to look at…the doctor took it to a waiting table, and the simple awful truth is that I managed a sideways, slanted glance and that was all. My heart skipped a beat, I felt a knot in my stomach—I had a gut feeling something significant had just happened—and I went back to attend to Susan, who, utterly exhausted, fell asleep and was wheeled back to her room.

I was alone in the corridor of this hospital, collecting my thoughts. I took a deep breath and decided there might be a baby involved in this business after all. So I plucked up my nerve, found the "preemie" nursery, and cautiously looked in. There were a few neonates in incubators, but I quickly found mine. At 5 1/4 pounds he was scraggly and thin, with ridiculous floppy ears and a head so stretched out that his entire little body could have been fit into a mailing tube.

They had dressed him in a nightgown and pinned the garment to the mattress beneath to keep him on his back. I think he was hooked to an intravenous tube. Of course he was crying. I put my pinky against his little palm and these oh-so-tiny fingers clenched, grasping me tightly. The denial evaporated as mist in the sun. Julian was born. With a feeling in my chest that was utterly new, I said hello. Still clutching my finger, he quieted down and ended his tears. And that's when mine began.

In retrospect, we could have immediately known that Julian had something wrong with him. Susan tried to breast-feed, even in the hospital, and Julian would not latch on. We thought it was because the hospital staff, on the very first day, had given him a bottle against our directions, and he had gotten used to that plastic nipple. It took Susan a full month of trying—a heroic effort that still impresses me—before Julian got the hang of it. Now we believe it was his low muscle tone that made the task of latching on particularly hard for him. In fact he has continually had difficulty working those muscles around his lips and mouth. It took him until age 6 to give up the nipple bottle and drink from a cup. He refuses to sip through a straw. And his diction remains poor to this day.

So, although we could have noticed there was something wrong with our son from birth, we didn't. After all, every child develops at a different pace. He was 10 months old when we took him for a regular medical checkup, and our pediatrician quite smartly noticed he wasn't sitting properly. Nor was he crawling in an age-appropriate manner. She suggested we take him to a developmental pediatrician for an evaluation.

And it was this team of doctors and assorted medical people who looked and measured, poked and pried, clucked and pointed out anatomical abnormalities in Julian's palm and in his palate. There was some genetic malformation, they told us; they could not say what, and his development was not on track. They recommended he get immediate therapy.

Well, okay. Julian was Julian by then. He had plumped up quite nicely, and had mostly grown into his ears. He was no longer that scraggly tubular thing I could not watch being born. He was my son, and that happy paternal gene which makes fathers dotty over their children had kicked in. (Not that this is a sure thing. I was right to have some concern, because I can point to fathers of dear friends who were abusive to their sons, or bullies, or at best were disparaging and competitive.) If Julian had some slight physical anomalies, who didn't? If he needed a few months of therapy, that was all right with me. After all, he was born a month early. If he had some delays now, he'd catch up. He'd be fine.

I mentally kicked back and relaxed. With my worst nightmare poking about the perimeter of my mind, my denial had returned, and thank goodness for it.

Susan was the one with the day job, with the regular salary that paid the rent. I was the one who "worked" from home. In our early discussions we thought that after our child's birth and a few months of maternity leave, Susan would return to her office 3 days a week, and work the other 2 days from home.

That schedule lasted about 2 months. The first few weeks back at work, Susan did stay home 2 days. Then it was 1 day. Finally, she was so behind at the office that she went back to work full time, and I was full-time dad.

Which, curiously, I did not mind. I had had this idea that if I ever became a father I'd get interested in my child when it was 2 or 3 years old, when it could talk, and we could have discussions and I could teach it things. I thought babies were lumps that drank bottles, cried, and needed to be changed. I thought the period of my child's infancy would be an uninteresting chore for me, at best.

Don't blame me, I didn't know. For all you men who are not fathers and who are reading this—and I am sure there are at least two of you— let me tell you what I learned. Babies are fascinating. They are smart, and they communicate all the time. They tell you exactly what they want and what they don't want. They are constantly investigating their environment, and that means stairs and scissors and keys and coins and you. Everything they can grasp goes into their mouths so you have to watch carefully, and it helps if you don't mind a finger in your nose or eye because they really want to know what things are, and they learn by touching.

I was also astonished to learn how much there was to do with a newborn. Don't ask what it was. I have no memories of how those days were filled. I only remember that Susan would call in the afternoon, and I would still be in pajamas.

So we had this early, unspecified diagnosis: Julian had developmental delays, and we were entitled to enroll him in a wonderful and wise program New York provides called Early Intervention. Any child from birth to 3 years—with diagnosed delays—can receive therapy at no cost to the family. The wisdom here is that if the state can catch and treat these delays early, it will save money later as the child enters the school system.

So, Julian began physical therapy, speech therapy, and occupational therapy. I always wondered about that last one. Occupational therapy for a 1-year-old? Well, it turns out that a delayed 1-year-old does have "occupational" tasks to master: to increase fine motor skills, to hear and begin to process language, to acquire social skills such as turn-taking. (My learning curve was as steep as Julian's.)

It was tiring, but one does what one needs to do. People manage in all kinds of difficult, exhausting situations, and there were plenty of parents with children worse off than Julian—children with seizures, children in wheelchairs with cerebral palsy, children with autism disorder who would not relate. Julian was smart, I could see it in his eyes. And this problem was temporary. He would catch up.

At 20 months he hadn't caught up. He was cruising around, holding on to furniture, but not yet walking, and he didn't have many words. I was still sure there was nothing really wrong, but we were not going to bury our heads in the sand. It was time to have Julian genetically tested. I remember the geneticist listing five or six possible reasons for the delays, conditions they would test for. One was a thyroid problem,

I can't recall the others. But the last one he mentioned was fragile X syndrome, which neither Susan nor I had heard of. I clearly recall him saying he hoped it wasn't that, because that was the only one on the list we couldn't treat.

We had the test in mid-December. They tied my little boy's arm to a board as they drew blood. I loosely held him and put my head to his belly to soften his cries. I actually don't think Julian experiences pain at the same level a typical child does; it seems he has a high tolerance for pain. But for sure he didn't like being tied down, and he wailed.

They said we would have the test results in a month. After two months with no word, I was convinced something was wrong. They had gotten bad news, and were running the test twice, to be sure. So when Susan called that February day and told me our son did in fact have fragile X syndrome, a piece of me was prepared to hear that. But, after I hung up the phone, I still screamed aloud, and I threw myself on our bed and I wept.

A word on sensitivity and crying: At a recent national fragile X conference, at a fathers-group meeting, one dad asked if others had experienced what he had. Since the diagnosis of his son there had been a general "opening of the faucets," as he put it, easy and uncontrolled weeping at the oddest times, at movies for God's sake! There was general assent. There is no question that having a damaged child makes a parent more vulnerable and more emotional. With women, this is not an issue. With men it still is. Anger and rage, the emotions that lead to action and even violence, wear well on a man. What men are *not* supposed to show is emotional weakness, and certainly never in public. Well excuse me, but I ain't having it. Whether or not I have a boy with fragile X, or Down syndrome, or autism, or just a kid with a lisp, this is America and I can strap on my gun and bawl whenever I damn well please!

I had screamed and wept like that only once before, when my sister called 10 years earlier to tell me Dad had died that morning of a heart attack. It took me a few years to adjust to that, and the loss stays with me still. I had no idea how I was ever going to adjust to this. This little boy who I loved beyond rational bounds and would easily protect at the cost of my own life was damaged in a way that I did not understand and could not make right. My denial had no retreat. My best defense was gone. The geneticist had casually told us that some fragile X boys never talked. A quick perusal of the literature informed us that fragile X was the leading inherited cause of mental retardation. On the positive side, this syndrome would not affect Julian's physical health, nor his longevity. Only his mental life.

Only his mental life.

This to a dad whose grade school IQ scores ranged...well, let's just say they were high enough to guarantee I would never live up to my potential. This to a dad whose twin heroes were Einstein and Freud, who had equal passion for trying to understand the complexities of the universe and the human mind. I announce this not to brag—every reader of this page will do better financially than I did this year—but to let the reader know I had a mental life that provided me with stimulation and pleasure, and I had hoped, I had expected, that this avenue through life, this joy of understanding and education and thought, would be at the basis of my bond with my son.

I didn't have a Plan B.

I floundered making an adjustment. Not in loving him—this should be abundantly clear and if it is not, let me make it so. Damaged or not, he was my perfect little boy. And I must say that happily this piece of news did not then or now affect my relationship to Susan. This is not always the case; parents of children with disabilities have all the normal stresses of family life, and then they have a challenging child. Blame, guilt, shame, ego, disappointment, money: the pressures can bring a couple closer together, or just as easily tear them apart. Yes, it was Susan's X chromosome, in him, that was damaged. So? If there was such a thing as fragile Y, it would have been mine. Neither of us knew she carried that mutation. I don't think she feels any guilt. Why should she? Susan and I are similar in that we don't trade in guilt and blame. I know it exists. I've seen it around me. I'm Jewish, after all. But however my parents might have felt guilt themselves, they don't seem to have instilled it in their children. And Susan hasn't acquired it from her family either, as near as I can tell.

Plan B did emerge, but it took time. It was an evolutionary process that may simply be another incarnation of denial and rationalization, but this time I think not. I am more of the opinion that Plan B, for all parents of disabled children, is, or in the best of circumstances can be, a transcendence. Let me explain.

Although I was apprehensive enough about fatherhood to deny it in the deadly-serious-yet-comical way I described above, in quite another sense I was ready not only to have a child, but, curiously, to have *this* child. Smart as I was, in 53 years I had learned that "smart" was not that important. Success, as commonly defined, was not that important. Although one does have to pay rent or the mortgage, money certainly was not that important. Ego was not important, nor worrying about the future or regretting the past.

So what was important?

Good was important. Kind was important. Honest was important. Being collegial and cooperative with fellow workers instead of competitive was important. Taking care of others was important, but equally important was accepting our own vulnerabilities and dependencies. Living in the moment was important, because the moment is all we have. And, of course, loving was important. And as I raised myself along with my son, I could see that despite all his disability and incompetence, Julian contained, quite naturally, everything I held to be important.

He was, indeed and ironically, my perfect little boy. He will probably need to be looked after, in some ways, for the rest of his life. But he will repay that kindness by educating others, by offering lessons that can be gained nowhere else.

And now I speak for all our children.

For anyone willing to look, our children are models. Not of competency, but of the qualities that transcend competence. If we care to look, our children teach us to be patient and kind and loving. If we care to look, our children show us how to take deep pleasure in the experience of the moment. If we care to look, our children teach us to never take anything for granted, and to find infinite joy in unimagined places. I know all parents are pleased when their child is toilet trained, but how many parents have their hearts near burst with pride when their son, at age 7, achieves this milestone for the first time and celebrates by taking a dozen bows? Even today, 3 years later, when I am in the house alone with Julian, I get a rush of pleasure at the sound of a distant toilet flushing.

Susan and I joke that Julian lives on another planet. My problem is that I like his planet. It is filled with songs and laughter and utterly unjustified self-confidence and hugs. My problem is that I am always just a little conflicted about working so hard to get this boy to be like everyone else, because I suspect our world would be a better place if everyone else were a little more like him.

I'm not sure that this is transcendence, but it is something a little better than denial. And it isn't Plan A, but it will do very nicely.

Connection In A Fragile World

Elizabeth Griffin is the mother of a son with fragile X and the author of **Fragile X, Fragile Hope: Finding Joy in Parenting a Child with Special Needs**.

Tentatively I left my 5-month-old in the nursery for the first time and entered the sanctuary of our church. The service began and I settled in, joining the singing of one of my favorite hymns. Then, despite a distance equal to a football field with three walls in between, my ear recognized his cry and my heart began pounding. A moment later the electronic monitoring system on the far wall flashed **8**, Zack's assigned number. It was my signal to come and get him. Moments later he was safely snuggled in my arms and content.

It was years before he let me sit through an entire church service. Some might have viewed my second-born son's severe separation anxiety as a sign of an attachment disorder. I only knew that his well-being desperately depended on me. Just as a delicate flower withers within a day for lack of water, it seemed as thought Zachary would fade away completely without my continuous effort to bring him to life.

Our first special education teacher tried to explain. "He lacks communicative intent," she said. In regular language this means that

Zack never asked for anything; he didn't know how to tell the world what he needed. Her words completely shocked me. I had no idea that Jay and I had unconsciously programmed ourselves to anticipate Zack's needs and meet them without a single gesture or word from him. Zack had trained us well.

It was then that we began the long journey of teaching our son to communicate. Thousands of dollars and hundreds of therapy hours later, he learned how to hand us a picture to tell us he was hungry and wanted a fish cracker. Later, he learned to sign "more" and hand over the picture. And, eventually, he learned to say, "I want fish, please." Still, at age 8, his preferred way of letting us know this vital information is to take us by the hand and pull us over to the pantry where the fish crackers are kept.

A Sunday School teacher accurately described the situation when she said, "For someone who doesn't talk, Zack's really good at telling you what he wants." Despite his lack of vocabulary, Zack's behavior indicates that he understands the majority of words we speak to him.

Being able to communicate on a basic level is a vital skill, but it is a sliver of what I really wanted, which was connection. The wonderful zest of having fun together, of laughing, singing, playing. That's what I was going for.

Take the eyes, for instance. We are trained as young children to look people in the eye. It shows we're listening, we're confident, we're connected. My firstborn, Taylor, and I used to play a game called "One eye, Two eyes." It went like this: He sat on my lap facing me and we moved our faces close together until we could see only one eye. Then we shouted, "One eye!" Next, we pulled away from each other until we saw two eyes, and—you guessed it—shouted, "Two eyes!" This provided hours of entertainment. Its purpose (other than learning to count to two) was, of course, connection.

I went through the gyrations of a snake handler many times a day to gain a fleeting glance from Zack. Lack of eye contact was on the top of my worry list. How do you connect with someone who doesn't talk and won't look at you? How do you even know they can hear you, or that you are part of their world? Of all the losses that fragile X syndrome threatened me with, this was the one I simply could not accept. I couldn't live without connecting with my child. I had to find a way to scale the sky-high wall that stood between us.

Desperation fueled my creativity. When Zack sat in his high chair, arms waving and voice loudly proclaiming "AHHHHHHHHHHHHH" until I thought I would scream, I did a little dance or moved toward him with a slinking motion to make him giggle. His delightful sense of humor gave me many a half-minute of respite from the very noisy world of a nonverbal child. And, it's been the sledgehammer that broke down the walls to let me into Zack's world. If you can't talk, laugh.

One night when Zack was 4, he sat on my knees facing me. We were giggling and bouncing around when he started making a "hm hm" sound. I repeated it back to him and he laughed uproariously. We spent the next thirty minutes "hm hm hm hming" back and forth in various rhythms and pitches. It was a game that went on for months, our first extended communication.

At 5, Zack pulled his shirt up over his face and giggled. "Where's Zachary?" I sing-songed. Quickly pulling his shirt down, he replied, "Boo boo, I see lu!" It was the first complete sentence he had spoken, and it told me all I needed to hear. He did see me! I was a part of his world.

After that I decided I was on Zack's radar screen even when he wouldn't look directly at me. This changed the way I talked to him. I spoke more often, and I spoke as if he understood, whether or not he gave an indication of it. It soon became apparent that he did, because he always responded to my antics and he began to follow simple directions.

There have been many sentences since that first one, 3 years ago—but I still have to remind myself from time to time that Zack hears me. If I begin acting like he doesn't, it isn't long until he lets me know.

It's 7:20 a.m. and we're into our usual routine. "Zack, the bus is almost here. Time to put on your socks and shoes."

"I know," he mumbles, face pointed toward his chest.

Handing them to him, I repeat, "Here, sweetie, put on your socks."

"I know," he again mumbles into his chest.

"Here Zack, your socks," I say, holding them out for him to take.

"I KNOW," he says, this time loud and clear.

I stand and watch him put them on. Then, as he walks past me, I say, "Now, get your shoes."

"STOP IT." He speaks with a volume that would make any speech therapist proud.

The other day a giggling, purple-fleece blanket came up to me and said, "Where's Zack?" I grabbed the edge and lifted it to reveal a shiny-eyed, smiling face framed with curls. "There he is!" I said. When I pulled the blanket over my head so we were both covered, Zack began rolling his fists, one in front of the other, and said, "Wheels on the bus?" I obliged, knowing I'd been caught in his never-ending pursuit of a singing partner. After the initial stanza, we went straight into Zack's favorite, "The people on the bus go up and down." He laughed as if he were hearing it for the first time and jumped up and down with glee.

There, in the dim light of the tent we'd made, I locked eyes with my little boy. Though his body has grown so the top of his head rests under my chin now, he is still a preschooler inside. Full of hugs and kisses for his "monny," he is often eager to play, to laugh, to love. Our times together are full of zesty connection. The thin thread between us has become a thick, multi-plaited cord, a link that will never snap or unravel.

My Boy's First Day At Baseball

Randy Weaver, the father of three, has one child who is a carrier of fragile X and one who has the full mutation.

My son Zach experienced "organized" baseball for the first time at age 5. Zach has fragile X syndrome and has played lots of sports, but this was the one that started it all. It's a small miracle that we continued in any sporting events after this initial test.

He donned his jersey, his glove, and a huge smile. For the past two days he had been saying "Smack! First base!" Translation: hit the ball squarely with proper hip rotation and run to first base.

Transitions can be a real problem for kids with fragile X and particularly for Zach, but he managed to transition well to get to the field through the crowd of energetic kids and parents loaded with lawn chairs, siblings, and coolers. The combination practice and game was 90 minutes long and took place during his normal lunchtime. That being the case, I knew he would "lose it" at some point. It wasn't a matter of "if" but of "when." My wife was not able to come and I had Zach's older sister Amanda and younger brother Josh in tow. Amanda had the green light to "sit on Josh if necessary" whenever I needed to regroup Zach.

His first time up in practice Zach made a great hit and ran to first base, giving me a high five on arrival. One base down, three transitions to go. The trip to second base was surprisingly smooth and calm as well, but it brought a look of concern to his face. Third base was more difficult and his hand was in his mouth by the time he pulled up to the base. Touching home plate brought a whine and a covering of the eyes. All in all, it was not bad for a first trip around the diamond.

Fielding was Zach's favorite activity and the coach was amused by the way he would hold out his mitt, turn his head, and cover his eyes when he was thrown a pop fly. Zach still does this at age 14. I give that coach credit for making sure Zach never got hit in the head.

All was well until the actual "game" started. There was a fair amount of commotion and four transitions within 5 minutes, which left Zach in the outfield crying and hugging me. One of the other moms asked, "Rough day?" To which I replied, "Rough life." While I was regrouping Zach, Amanda was curled up, wrapped in our blanket, taking it easy while 2-year-old Josh waded in a puddle knee-deep, with two moms trying to coax him out of the middle of the large body of water. I could also see they were wondering where the idiot parents of this child were. Not to worry, I was close by and monitoring the situation with my astute peripheral vision. I was proud of Zach as he struggled to keep his composure. His at-bat consisted of a swing, a well-hit ball, a smile, a cheer from the crowd, and an over-stimulated burst of tears. He ran to first base and just kept running, crying, into my arms. By this time, I was holding him and his brother, soaked to the bone, with ten parents staring at me thinking (or so I assumed), "What kind of parent are you?" I watched the rest of the parents pick up their items, seemingly so relaxed, and I was jealous.

The teams then lined up for high fives and Zach bounced (as he often does when over-stimulated) and yelled, "High five, high five!" as he slapped hands with the other kids, hugging a couple of them. I looked at some of the kids as they sauntered through the line with boredom. Their parents routinely completed packing their gear for them. I heard Zach, still yelling: "High five, high five!" Then I gave him a hug, which he returned. He had worked harder and consequently got more from that day than anyone else who attended.

I wasn't jealous anymore.

An Australian Story

Nicola Jones lives in Australia and has a daughter and two siblings with fragile X syndrome.

My name is Nicola Jones and my husband, Rick, and I have two daughters. The eldest is 6 years old and the other is nearly 3. Our big girl, Maddie, has full mutation fragile X syndrome. The younger child, Jordan, doesn't, nor is she a carrier.

I feel we are among the lucky ones, as our daughter was diagnosed when she was just 2. In Australia, diagnosis is often delayed as fragile X syndrome is not usually mentioned in early discussions with doctors or specialists. They seem to be more focused on autism or attention deficit disorder. Due to this early diagnosis, we were able to begin with interventions. Also, as I had fallen pregnant at the same time Maddie was diagnosed, we were able to have a chorionic villus sampling (CVS) test to determine our second child's status. Since this diagnosis, my 30-year-old brother and my 32-year-old sister have both tested positive for full mutation and I am a premutation carrier at 39. However, our journey began with Maddie.

As a baby, Maddie had very bad reflux. She had to have a strict routine and was very uncomfortable around other people. As she grew, she would gag on solid food. She hated loud noises and didn't like going to unfamiliar places. Maddie didn't walk until she was two, she had very poor gross motor skills, and didn't like playing with other children. Her attention span varied from 5 seconds to around 5 minutes. As these milestones were considered slow, we consulted our doctor who luckily referred us to a switched-on pediatrician. This is where luck came in. This specialist tested for fragile X syndrome as a matter of course.

Maddie was sent for a blood test and while we waited for the results, we did some research. The Fragile X Association of Australia has a very good Web site, www.fragilex.org.au, and Maddie had so many of the behavioral characteristics that we were sure she had fragile X. Rick and I were also tested and sure enough, Maddie was full mutation and I was the carrier. I had mixed emotions. On one hand, I was relieved that we had a "label" for Maddie's condition—something to tell people when they asked why Maddie behaved the way she did and something to tell the professionals so they would be able to help her. On the other hand, we felt we were given a "life sentence." Maddie would not get better, she might even get worse. She may need constant supervision and not be able to look after herself. Would she talk, go to a regular school, get a job, have relationships and friends, have a family? These were questions we had for the genetic counselors. Fortunately, we managed to get an appointment with Dr Ann Turner, who gave us answers to these and many other queries about the syndrome. We left feeling a little more informed and ready to face the problems head-on.

This is where I have to go back to my brother and sister. My sister passed all of her milestones. She was very quiet, a little shy but no more so than many other young girls. She coped fairly well at school, though not brilliantly, and her mathematics skills left a lot to be desired. I remember trying to teach her how to count money. She just couldn't grasp the concept. The same with time. She still prefers a digital watch and clock. She has held a job since leaving school, a job that nobody would have thought possible—a cashier—and she has to be one of the most reliable and trustworthy workers ever. She has her driver's license and lives in a small townhouse by herself, though close to our mother and father. She isn't very social, she prefers her own company, watching movies and reading, but she seems happy.

My brother had trouble from an early age. At around 18 months my mother commented to the early childhood nurse that she thought he had problems with his feet. They seemed to turn inwards. She was referred to a specialist who suggested he wear special boots with a bar joining them together so his feet would "learn" to face in the right direction. I can't remember how long that lasted but it wasn't a nice thing to see a small baby pulling himself along with his feet bolted together. The next thing was his allergies. He always had a stuffed-up nose. The doctors did the "prick test" to find out what he was allergic to. The results showed him to be allergic to most things. He was taken off yeast and dairy products. Toilet training took forever and he was still wetting the bed at 12 years old. He had trouble at school with his studies. Reading and writing were difficult and mathematics was impossible, but all his reports show that he tried very hard and was a very nice child to be around. I remember him being invited to birthday parties, so he had friends. I also remember him biting his hand whenever he was upset or frustrated. All the while, the specialists kept saying, "we don't know what is wrong; he must have had a difficult delivery," or, "it is just a global delay."

Once in high school, he was placed in a special class. This was a system they were trying out in this particular school, where special needs kids have their own class within a normal school so they get to integrate with mainstream children. That school now has several special classes and positions are sought after by many parents for their kids. The teacher who first taught my brother is now in charge of the whole system. It has worked extremely well and the kids are very well accepted.

My brother stayed at school until he was around 16. He then did a series of courses at the local technical college. He became involved in a disability service where his employer was subsidized by the government to assist him in learning job skills, and he coasted along until my parents decided to move to a country town on the coast of New South

Wales. They moved with my brother and sister and set up a small farm with Angora goats for my brother to tend and earn money from the fleece. I must admit that this was the best move for my siblings. Less people, fewer frustrations, no stress. My sister got her driver's license, and after many lessons my brother did too. He is still involved with the disability service and they got him a position at the local bowling club. He sets tables, prepares vegetables, and washes the dishes. The staff are all fantastic and include him in everything. He has become quite independent though he still lives with our parents. He even went out and got a couple of tattoos.

Neither my brother or my sister received any interventions to assist them with their development. I often wonder how things would have turned out if they had. Nor did they have fragile X syndrome as their diagnosis.

On the other hand, Maddie has had the benefit of every intervention we could get. Occupational therapy, physiotherapy, speech therapy, and social skills training, as well as our decision to become part of the Fragile X Association of Australia. We thought that would be the best way to get information as it became available. Through this organization, we were able to meet people and discuss issues relating to our daughter as well as swap some very amusing tales. I also learned how carrier women could be affected with some of the symptoms. Growing up, I suffered anxiety, stress, and mild panic attacks. I needed routine and structure and was painfully shy. Until this time, I thought all these things were normal. Now, after some medication, my life has become more enjoyable.

My parents are learning more about fragile X syndrome through living with my brother and understanding his needs. My mother is only starting to come to terms with the guilt she feels from passing on the damaged X chromosome, something she had no way of knowing about, and something we do not blame her for.

Maddie started school this year, and due to the fabulous work that many people have put in, the transition has been very successful. I now have some time to contribute to our Association too. I have joined one of the Association's committees and would love to see others join so they can benefit like I have. Our committee runs the Sydney Fragile X Clinic, which treats both children and adults, produces a quarterly newsletter, undertakes all forms of fundraising, and organizes conferences. While all this is very hard work, there are bonuses like meeting and dining with such people as Randi Hagerman, Marcia Braden, and Lesley Powell, just to name a few. Because we are so involved, we get a lot of information as soon as it comes to hand. I realize that people with children who have fragile X have many day-to-day issues to deal with. I also understand that these people may very well have issues with being a carrier or even being affected themselves. What better way is there to face your issues than with people who have the same ones as you do? You can laugh, you can cry, you can be embarrassed, you can even have the worst anxieties, and you will not feel out of place.

Wherever you are, there is an Association for you. If you are in Australia, you are more than welcome to join ours; we would love to see you. If you are overseas, make an effort to get involved and help to spread the word about fragile X syndrome where you are living.

Fragile Decisions

Elizabeth Appell, an award-winning author, playwright, and screenwriter, wrote this short story especially for **X Stories**.

The list was entitled "Four Reasons Not To Have Children." One. Children make terrible messes. Two. Children smell. Three. They are unrelentingly demanding. Four. They undermine a mother's sense of self-worth.

My mother, Maxine, presented me with this list during the last weekly canasta lunch with her sister, Trudy. The routine was to eat egg salad sandwiches and deal cards at the same time. I had been included in order to celebrate Maxine's latest "hair action." "Hair action" meant that once again Maxine had changed the color of her mane. Today it vibrated with a definite violet tinge.

"The same color as Elizabeth Taylor's eyes," she said, and then presented the list. I think the list was given to me between hands because I had just announced that I'd met a man that I actually liked.

"What's his name?" Maxine asked.

"David," I said.

"David what?" she said. "Every David I've ever known has had a last name." As usual she waved off my answer and downed her martini.

Then she opened her worn alligator bag and pulled out a page torn from a legal tablet, separating at the folds. She must have been carrying the list for years in preparation for my announcement. David wasn't my first boyfriend, but somehow Maxine knew he'd be the last.

"Maxine, leave the girl alone," Trudy said. Trudy was a gaunt woman whose hair had gone white when she was in her twenties. She wore it in a French Resistance haircut. I could easily see her dressed in fatigues with a rifle slung over her shoulder. Trudy's house was down the street from ours. The sisters picked at each other like preening monkeys, but they would never live more than five blocks apart. "Kids aren't so bad," Trudy said. She laid down two cards and drew two. "Finally they go away."

My mother rolled her eyes. "Yours came back," she muttered. "Imagine, thirty-three and Clay's home living with his mommy."

"You're just jealous. Tomasina would set herself on fire before moving back home with you. Am I right, baby?" Trudy looked at me. "Well, am I?"

She was right. I adored my mother, and wished I had what it took to wear violet hair, but I would never live with her again. If I did I knew I'd end up on death row.

My mother laid down her hand. "Canasta," she said. "I won't say it again. Don't have children." Then she said, "Tommy, listen to me." She hesitated long enough to pick her teeth with a Canasta card. "They rob you of sleep, steal your security, make you feel like a failure, and break up your marriage."

"Why aren't those items on your list?" I asked.

"They are," she said. "Turn the page over." Sure enough. There was another list carefully inscribed with four more warnings.

"How come the X thing isn't on the list?" I said.

At first I didn't understand the hitch in the chatter that my comment had created, and then it clicked. My question had brought up the sisters' unspoken subject: Catherine. Catherine was Trudy's mildly retarded 28-year-old daughter. Though it had taken almost 16 years for the diagnosis to be made, Catherine had been born with fragile X. After that, both

Maxine and Trudy had been tested and came up positive. Though I didn't have fragile X, what were the odds that I was a carrier?

Maxine cleared her throat, and then tossed out, "I don't think we have to write it down."

I fanned myself with the list, and then asked if I had done all the things she had listed.

Her answer: "Every one of them."

I shrugged and finished off my egg salad. I knew she was different from other women and I liked that. When I entered the third grade, early in the school year, one of the mothers called. My mother mimicked the woman's voice. "Sorry, Maxine. We'll drive Tommy to school, but you're out. You're just not carpool material." I had crowed with pride.

When I turned twelve, I came home to find that she had baked cookies. I cried. "Now you're just like all the other moms."

Maxine laid out a column of cards. "Truth be known, I may have left your father even if you hadn't come along."

So when David asked me to marry him, I said I would if we first could come to an understanding that we would never have children. Only dogs and only from shelters. No breeders. They would be mature dogs, dirty and flea-bitten. Fear should show in their eyes and they should be wary of approaching their food. We would save them.

Six months later I got pregnant. We'd done nothing about getting a dog and everything, I thought, about not getting a baby.

"You're going to have a baby, dear," Dr. Toinby said.

"Don't call me 'dear,'" I said. "And I want you to change the course of things this minute."

He looked at me over his granny glasses. One eye was glass. "Not until you consult with your husband, dear. It takes two to tango. Go home, dear, and have a nice little chat."

That afternoon instead of working on the copy for the ad campaign I'd just been hired to write—the product was mud from the Dead Sea to be used for facial treatments—I sat on the bottom step of our circular staircase and waited for David to come home from work. I knew he'd enter with his tie loosened at the neck, scuffed briefcase in hand, and his breath smelling of scotch. All defense lawyers drink at lunch. I decided that the only way to approach him without entering into all-out war was to tread gently and remain calm.

He walked through the door.

"Damn you! *Damn you!* You made me pregnant!" I grabbed a down pillow from the couch and hammered it against him until the feathers floated like small birds.

Tears squirted out of my eyes, and when I wiped them away, I found mascara on my fingertips. His pale blue eyes opened in a striking expression of innocence.

Looking back, he must have been expecting my tirade, because he didn't fend me off or say a word. Nor did he speak when I threw the cold vegetarian stew at him. Clumps of tomatoes stuck to his white button-down shirt like blood clots. He was about to speak when the doorbell rang. I recognized the voice at the door to be that of Craig, our neighbor. Craig, a finely tuned effeminate man, would probably give his eyeteeth to have a vagina, breasts, and babies.

"Nothing's wrong," David said. "Just a small celebration. We're pregnant!"

I peeked around the corner.

"What's that stuff on your shirt?" Craig asked.

"Pretend afterbirth. We're practicing," David said. Craig shivered, waved wanly, and left.

"I'm not going through with it," I said, my molars pulverizing the words. "It's a sin to have a baby when you're crippled."

"Who's crippled?" David said. "I don't see any blue handicap signs around here."

"Me," I said. "I'm an emotional cripple. I love Maxine, but daily it's a struggle to survive daughterhood. Motherhood is a flat-out impossibility."

"Your mother will set you straight," David said.

"She won't be around," I said. "I'm going to dispose of her."

"I love it when you get into one of your ironic dark funks," he said. His mouth spread into a sly grin. It's so...." He hesitated.

"Existentially bent?" I said.

"Exactly," he said.

"I won't do it," I said. "I'm getting rid of it in the morning. Tomorrow I'm going to a clinic and get the little bugger sucked out!"

David darkened and turned away. I pulled my sweater down over my stomach. Nothing showed. "Aren't you going to try and stop me?" I whispered. "A small attempt?" When he turned back, his hands gripped into fists.

Just when the last of my energy was about to leak onto the carpet, and I no longer could speak without my voice sounding like sandpaper, David sat heavily down on the couch. Feathers fluttered around him.

"What?" I said.

He looked at me. A secret hid behind his eyes and he pressed his palms together as if praying and tapped his mouth.

"You're keeping something from me," I said.

He shook his head.

"Damn it," I railed. "I know you. You don't fold your hands in prayer because, as far as I know, you don't pray! For Christ's sake, tell me." He opened his mouth to speak, but then closed it. "God damn it, David. You *know* you're going to tell me." His fingers tapped. "You know you're going to." Tap. "Oh, just shut up!" I screamed.

By the expression on his face, I knew I was about to be whacked.

"I pricked holes in the condoms." His face was open like a tunnel. I could have driven through that expression with a Mack truck. "One way or the other, I wanted a child."

The betrayal was so stunning I could barely speak. I managed to say, "It takes two to tango, bud." The words came without breath. Then I gulped out, "We'll go to the pound tomorrow. A filthy rabid year-old German shepherd should do the trick." Nausea churned in my gut and rose to my throat.

David went into the kitchen. I followed. Methodically he scraped stew off his shirt.

"I wonder what it feels like to love someone who doesn't throw things," he said.

"Right," I said. "Another good reason for a dog. You throw for them."

"I want to love someone who has the capacity to emotionally progress past the age of five, somebody who can say, 'I love you,' and mean it."

Avoiding the tomato mess, I came up from behind and put my arms around his waist. "I think you're swell," I said, and kissed him on the neck.

"Does that mean you love me?"

"You bet."

"Do you mean it?" he said.

"No." I started to cry again. "You didn't play fair, and for that I'll never be able to trust you. From now on, if I say anything nice to you, don't believe it. I want you to know what it feels like not to be able to trust."

Exhausted, I crawled into bed. My eyes stung and they felt swollen. I put my head on the pillow, and immediately fell into a dark, deep place, into a pit, or into a crack in the earth's crust, or an ocean. My throat had a door in it that shut and I couldn't breathe. When I opened my mouth to scream, all that came out was, "Here, take my hand."

It was a small voice that came out of me, a very young voice, light, buttery, unused. It spoke again. "Go on, take it."

I was drowning in the darkness, so I had no choice. I reached out. A tiny hand wrapped around my pointer finger, and a small presence with amazing strength pulled me up. Up toward the light, like a cormorant shooting through seawater, up toward brightness, up closer to the skin of what separated me from air. Up to ripples and shadows. Up as ropes of bubbles followed us. Up toward the surface, a window of handblown glass, wavy and uneven and just on the other side I could see a figure pacing. Up we swam until we reached the other world. Cups of sunshine floated on the surface, and then we broke through. I was starving. Ravenous.

I gulped and opened my eyes. The dark ocean turned into daylight. I kicked off the covers and then reached out to touch David, but he had already risen. I could hear him downstairs, banging in his shop, hammering something wooden.

I climbed out of bed, slipped into my flannel robe and went down. The new sun bled through the shop window, a shaft of light crossed the workbench. He bent over a piece of wood and hammered nails, one after the other.

"What're you building?" I asked.

He looked up at me, as if surprised to see that I was the one standing in his doorway. "Nothing," he said. "I'm building absolutely nothing."

"I'm going to make coffee. Maybe cook some eggs," I said.

"You shouldn't eat before you go," he said. "It's an operation, you know. You shouldn't eat."

I went to the downstairs bathroom and peed. David stood outside the door.

"You shouldn't eat," he said again, as if my not eating had become his job for the day.

I spoke to him from the bathroom. "I met him. He saved me. We'll have him."

"What?" he said.

I came out shrugging my flannel shoulders. "I owe him that."

David tried to embrace me, but I pulled away. "Epiphanies are interesting," I said. "Instructive, actually. We'll have this child. Afterwards I'll keep working and you can stay home and raise him."

David looked at me for a long time and then he nodded. "Okay," he said. "All right." And then he pulled me into his arms and we slow-danced to a tune he hummed. Something I wouldn't imagine him to know. *Dream.* An Andrews Sisters' song, popular before both our times.

"So, my darling, how are you coping with the hormones?" my mother asked. Her hair glowed fluorescent pink. "Chin hairs sprouted yet?" I answered by running to the bathroom to vomit. She peeked in and smiled. "Goes with the territory."

During the first couple of months of my pregnancy, she stopped by often, usually unexpected. "Nesting yet? Craving Polish sausages at midnight? Hot for sex? I remember being pregnant with you. I couldn't get enough. You name it, I wanted it." She winked. "Since then, my zest has taken a back seat. Except for hair actions." Her veined hand cradled her curls.

"I'm fine," I said. Now her hair was brown with green highlights. "Different."

"Thanks," she said. "I've found a new hairdresser. Definitely queer, but he doesn't hate women as much as the last one."

"Gay, Maxine. Not queer. Anyway, I meant me. I feel different."

"Oh, of course you do. There's a creature inside gobbling you up at an astounding pace." I did a save on my computer. The campaign was going well. My client said I had a natural inclination for Dead Sea mud.

"My edges are smoother," I said. "Not so sharp and...." I hesitated.

"I know," my mother said. "You already love this baby."

"Yes," I said, stunned. Love was not a part of her vocabulary. I smiled, because by sharing her insight, she inadvertently had linked the word to me. It was the first time I realized how my mother loved me. She loved me from a distance, but it was piercing and straight as a laser.

"Have you been tested?"

"No."

"Does David know?"

"No."

Maxine shoved her hands into her Bedford cords. "Tomasina, you mean you haven't told him?"

"We're the kind of people who have secrets," I said.

My mother combed her fingers through green highlights. Then she pulled her upper lip out and moved it side to side. It made her look like a kid doing funny faces.

"You have to tell him the risks. You have to tell him what it might mean."

"I don't know what it might mean and I don't want to know."

"You have to tell him, Tommy. You might be a carrier. I am."

Over his glasses Dr. Toinby studied us. I thought I could see my reflection in his false eye, but I decided it was my imagination. Before he spoke I knew the answer. Doctors don't drum pencils on their desks unless they are going to tell you something bad.

"The test was positive, dear," he said. "You typically have a fifty percent chance of giving birth to a boy with fragile X, and a fifty percent chance of having a girl who carries the fragile X gene."

I looked at David. A couple of nights before I had explained everything, but hearing it from the doctor had made it real. He paled and gulped for air as though he was scaling the last fifty feet of Everest. I reached out to him, but he was too far away.

Toinby stopped drumming and turned to David. "The syndrome is called fragile X, because a fragile site or gap exists at the end of the long arm of the X chromosome in the lymphocytes of the affected fetus."

"Does the baby die?" David asked.

I felt the depths of the ocean deepening.

"No. The lesser-affected children have mental impairment, attention deficit, hyperactivity."

"That's nothing," I said. "Nothing."

By now David had reached the top of the mountain and his breathing had slowed and was on the way to normalizing.

"And the others?" David said.

Toinby's one eye searched the ceiling for sanctuary; finding none, it came back to me. "It's the absence of the FMR1 protein that causes mental retardation, severe autistic-like behaviors, long face, large ears."

"Dumbo." I interrupted and felt a smile crack through my desperation. I started laughing, but the chuckles choked out more like sobs. "I'm going to give birth to Dumbo."

"Stop it," David barked at me.

My head snapped toward him. I wanted to scream, "I told you we shouldn't get pregnant. If this were a damn dog we could put it to sleep and get another one!" Instead I whispered, "I'm sorry," and blew my nose into a tissue.

"Do we know to what degree our baby will be affected?" David asked.

"We'll do a test for the absence of the protein at twelve-and-a-half weeks. The test is conclusive. The cells will have to be cultured. It might be a month or more before we have an answer." Toinby pushed his fingers over the pencil as if it were a rolling pin. "I've given you a lot to think about, dear."

"Don't call me dear!"

David gathered me up, nodded good-bye to the doctor, and we left his office. On the way out of the office, the moon-faced receptionist offered a faint smile and then passed us a note on a page torn from a prescription tablet. "I know a woman who teaches at a school where a couple of fragile X kids go. Call her." She had scribbled a name and a telephone number at the bottom.

Outside I breathed deeply. Once again I felt that little hand pulling me up from the drowning depths. My fingers moved over my stomach. "I think he's listening to us."

David kissed my cheek. "How do you know it's a boy?"

"I just do."

Neither of us could face going home, so we crossed the street and wandered into the park. The day was light and flowery. Spring, maybe. Early spring when things are new. Pigeons waddled in small packs, and an old lady scattered bread. They flew to her feet like one big bird. Children squealed as they romped, and mothers sat on benches watching their every move.

We sat down. I felt David's hand on my shoulder. "Let's go to the animal shelter today."

I nodded. I was willing, except my legs suddenly weighed a thousand pounds and I couldn't walk. "What are we going to do?"

I cried. "Fifty percent. Pretty lousy odds. My mother took them. Of course she didn't *know* the risks. The X thing wasn't part of the conversation back then."

David nodded. "You're right, the odds aren't so great." His body leaned against me. It felt kind.

We had made arrangements to meet with Maddie Connors, the special education teacher that Moon-Face had suggested. We arrived a little before first period at Hitchcock Heights Elementary School.

At first I thought we'd made a mistake. Hitchcock Heights looked like any other elementary school. As we made our way through the labyrinth of buildings, youngsters whooped and whirled around us in chaotic enthusiasm. None of these kids were retarded. No long-faced, big-eared kids here.

Following our instructions, we made our way to the back of the campus where there was an outbuilding. A stream of parents walked their youngsters toward this classroom, and it was evident that their kids were different.

David took my hand and we stepped in. The classroom was painted with muted pastels, and the aroma of freshly baked cookies wafted through the air. Indecipherable drawings by children were taped to the walls, two computers sat on a table, a cutout of the alphabet looped across the blackboard. An aquarium sat in the corner, a home for three tree frogs. Like any elementary school it was furnished with low tables and small chairs. On the tables were cans of crayons and trays of chalks, and near one of the walls was a roll of butcher paper.

A boy taller than the rest of the kids held up an envelope and bolted toward us. Though his speech was garbled, he made us understand his name, Kevin, and he explained that he had made a card for a teacher he clearly loved.

"Thank you for greeting our visitors, Kevin," said a woman who glowed from the inside. This was Maddie Connors, the woman we'd come to meet. Just as she reached out to shake my hand, chaos erupted at the door. Four more lively children escorted by parents entered. The level of noise and energy ramped up, and simultaneously, sun flooded through the bank of windows on the opposite side of the room. Once the parents left, I realized the other adults still in the room tenderly dealing with the youngsters were teachers. One teacher to every two students.

"The children in this class cut across the spectrum from mild to severely retarded," Maddie said. "And even the kids on paper that are supposedly hopeless, sometimes do amazing things. Kevin is not only autistic, but he's been abused. Then she pointed to a light bulb of a kid that definitely was switched on. "That girl has had several strokes and often has seizures in the classroom, but she's a delight. She's going to do just fine. This semester we only have one child diagnosed with fragile X."

There was a scuffle at the doorway. We all turned to see a handsome boy with deep blue eyes looking out of a tangle of long lashes. His cheeks were flushed, but he didn't have a long face or big ears. No Dumbo here, but there was little doubt that he was severely impaired. He bit one hand while the other hand twisted his hair, and all the while he looked elsewhere, avoiding eye contact with the people in the room.

"Darren," Maddie said. "Come on in and join us." Darren's mother had a brief conversation with Maddie, kissed Darren good-bye, and exited.

Darren immediately plopped down on the floor. I stepped toward him. He spewed a guttural moan toward me, then he jammed his hand into his pants and began to fumble.

"No hands, Darren." Maddie said. "You know we've talked about this." Maddie looked up at me and smiled. Her face shone and without words she said: *This is not a problem. None of these kids are problems. These children are perfect.*

"Are you ready for breakfast, Darren?" Maddie leaned toward the boy. "Are you hungry?"

His head nodded back and forth and drool seeped out of his mouth. Then he let go of a loud, hacking sound, agonizing, as though something deep inside his brain was working to get an idea out.

109

"How old are you, Darren?" I asked, crouching down in front of him.

"He's nine," Maddie said.

I thought she must be wrong. He was so small. I extended my hand.

"Darren's typical of a child with fragile X and goes from the extreme of not wanting to be touched at all, to requiring huge bear hugs."

"Hey, Darren," I said, leaving my arm extended. My heart enlarged as I watched Darren struggle to control the simple coordination it took to get his arm to move toward me. "How about a high five?" Darren raised his hand and I tapped it. "Great!" I said, and turned to David. "Wasn't that great?" David had become faceless and his head motioned toward the door, a movement that distinctly said, let's get the hell out of here.

The boy howled and then cackled.

Again I offered my hand. "Another high five?" Again Darren reached. "Good boy," I said. I looked up at my faceless husband. "Isn't he a good boy?"

Maddie lifted Darren, set him on his feet, and guided him toward the table with paper and crayons. "Yesterday he did a wonderful drawing."

A wan smile brought David's face back into focus and he loosened his tie. "I think we better be going," he said.

"But we haven't...."

He guided me out of the room. "Thank you," he called to Maddie as he held the door open for me.

"We can't have this baby," David said. We were standing outside the classroom. Through window glare I could see Maddie leaning over Darren, her hand on his, guiding him toward drawing a big circle. She straightened and looked out. Our eyes met. I knew what she was thinking. *One glimpse of a Darren and the decision is made.*

"No!" The word echoed silently in my head. I yearned to tromp back into the classroom and bellow, "The decision is not made!"

"We can try again," David said. "We'll have a baby."

"You did this, David. You poked the goddamn holes in the goddamn condom and now we're going to live with the possibility of the goddamn fragile X no matter what goddamn baby we make!"

"You want a Darren?" David steered me away from the classroom. As we reached the car I spotted a haggard woman rushing toward the school. Was she just a regular mother heading for a teacher-parent meeting, or was she a mother of one of the retarded kids? Maybe she was a carrier. Did she and her husband have to deal, day after day, with their Darren? Did they have to sit on the floor with their kid who painstakingly tried to make his fragile brain communicate with his beleaguered body, so he could manage to say, "I want to play"?

I slid into the car. David leaned down and whispered into my ear. "I trust you. You make the decision."

I lay my head on the pillow and immediately fell into that familiar dark ocean. The door in my throat shut as it had before and I couldn't breathe. When I opened my mouth to scream, the voice that came from me was the same small one, young and unused.

"We can make it."

I peered toward the surface. It seemed a long way away. My lungs began to burn and the ache in my chest felt like an impending explosion.

"Give me your hand," the small voice said. "Please, give me your hand."

I opened my mouth and inhaled. Cold water rushed in, a violent torrent, roaring, grinding, flushing out the past, flooding the future. I started kicking toward the surface, toward the sunlight and air, and the dark figure on the other side of the surface paced back and forth. The water was heavy, sluggish, and ran in the opposite direction than I wanted to go, but I kicked and the little hand tugged and we moved for all we were worth up toward the light.

And then. Finally. We broke through.

It was David who pulled me out of the surf and onto land. I vomited seawater. He wiped my face and kissed my nose and I awakened in our bed.

The telephone rang. David answered it. He cleared his throat, said thank you and hung up. "It was Toinby," he said. "We need to make an appointment with his receptionist. The test is in."

"It's in?" I said.

"Yeah," he said.

"No," I said. "We don't need to see him. I already know. The baby's fine. No matter what the test says. The baby's fine."

I could smell the sea, taste its brine on my lips, and hear its relentless waves beating at the shore. The sweet ocean rose. I felt its sting, as the small hand wrapped around my finger, pulling me up. I knew that we'd swim to the surface together.

Artist: Sharon Carter

Sharon Carter is an artist and writer who also holds a medical degree from Cambridge.

Transitions

Fragile X Code-Talkers

*Carolyn Ybarra, the stepmother of a 19-year-old man with
fragile X syndrome, is active in the Northern California Fragile
X Association.*

One day as we rode in the car, Jessie pointed out another car like
ours: "Subaru Outback…whale. It's a mammal!" I laughed in delight.
My 19-year-old stepson is developmentally delayed, and he's clever.
Playing with similar sounding words like humpback and outback
is something he does frequently and with enjoyment. Analogous
comparison is ever present in his view of the world, allowing such
humor to come to him readily. He loves silliness of every variety, enjoys
the sounds words make, and understands the most obscure puns. I find
this language ability fascinating, considering that at age 8 he spoke in
one word "sentences."

Whether they are our children or our students, figuring out how
best to interact with and teach children who have fragile X can be a
difficult challenge indeed. What is hard to convey is just how wonderful
it can be to get to know a child or adult with fragile X. Interacting with
these multifaceted children can be surprising, enlightening, joyous, and
sometimes life changing.

Perhaps this appeal is based in the great sense of humor many people with fragile X have. Their ability to imitate any and all sounds, cartoon voices, and animal noises—well, sometimes it just infects one with silliness. Their strength of memory for things that happened long ago—and places they have visited only once—comes as a surprise and a delight. Most moving and heart wrenching is a frequent characteristic of a person with fragile X: the incredible empathy that is likely a result of learning to deal with the serious problem of enhanced sensitivity to all types of sensory input. The power of this enhanced empathy becomes apparent when you realize someone who is supposed to be mentally challenged has just manipulated the pants off of you, and you didn't even notice.

One of the most intriguing characteristics of these boys and girls, men and women, is their unique approach to and understanding of language. Affected individuals fall within a broad range of abilities, with some not speaking at all and others able to talk in complete, complex sentences. Those who do speak share a manner of conveying information that I like to refer to as "fragile X code-talk." It's a kind of cipher that parents and teachers struggle to understand, yet it has its own inherent logic. I'd like to share some examples of the unique language used by our fragile X code-talkers.

Strength of memory, which characterizes those with fragile X, plays a part in the interest some boys with fragile X show in cars. This interest is based in the seemingly innate fascination boys of all ages and developmental stages have with cars. Identifying familiar cars is a favorite pastime for Jessie when he's on the road. Lately we both get a thrill when we see a Ford Aerostar and a Volkswagen Jetta at the same time. We used to own an Aerostar van, and he still waxes nostalgic about it 2 years later: "I miss my Aerostar," he says in a forlorn tone. "The blue van is goooone." His mother drives a Jetta. As soon as we spot an Aerostar and a Jetta together, we start in: "Aerostar, mommy's car, Aerostar, mommy's car!" We chant in unison, both enjoying the rhyme as well as the serendipity. This little game of ours combines a love of the familiar with a fondness for rhythm and rhyme. People with fragile X syndrome enjoy collections of similar objects, but we are able to "collect" our favorite automobiles without having to take them home.

Alex, also age 19, associates cars he sees with past events and familiar people, regardless of how much time has passed since the family or friend owned that particular car. When he was 4 years old, his family rented a car during a vacation. Today, 15 years later, whenever he sees that make and model he says, "Mom, remember, that's what we rented when we were in Michigan." He associates the automobile with the vacation, the place, and the story in the family's past. It may be that the car is a mnemonic used to bring back an entire set of circumstances. The car is the associative identifier that triggers the memory and story of a person or an entire event.

Ben, age 17, talks to cars and their drivers when he is riding in the car. When a car pulls in front of his family's car, he'll say: "Excuse me sir, you go, you can go." He also expresses his emotions through his interactions with cars. When he is walking down the street with his family, if he is feeling very content, he will stop at a car, pet it, and give it a kiss. "Sweet baby car," he says, to express his happiness. Other parents of children with fragile X will have their own kissing and licking stories, a particular favorite being the fruit at the grocery store. Jessie similarly invests many inanimate objects with a personality, heart, and soul. He talks to them, or makes them "talk," each with its own voice.

Jessie thinks and talks like a poet: in rhythm, analogies, metaphors, and imagery. Like reading poetry, when I talk with him I don't always understand his original intent and meaning, but I know art when I see it. Sometimes, as with poetry, a few words are imbued with a deep richness of meaning that I strive to decipher. One word stands for many, and a sentence represents a paragraph. Sometimes, not as often as when he was younger, I can't understand the words at all. Usually I correctly guess his meaning, because I know him well, and I know to look to both sides of what he says to find his reference point. If he wants to talk about the bush, you'll find him beating around it.

In the same way that he doesn't look a person directly in the eye while talking, my stepson doesn't address conversational topics directly. He approaches them obliquely. The "gaze aversion" is based in sensory issues typical to fragile X syndrome. Meeting another's eyes is just too raw an experience to tolerate. It is possible that approaching a topic head-on is similarly too direct and too intense, so that topics are more easily approached from the periphery, a sort of "topic aversion." This conversational gambit occurs most often in anxiety-producing contexts. Although perhaps ultimately sensory-related, topic aversion is more clearly related to anxiety.

When he is anxious about a transition, Alex uses topic aversion instead of just saying, "I don't want to go." Transitions are commonly difficult for people with fragile X, who find it hard to move from one place or activity to another. Favorite statements in this context are "Maybe they canceled it" or "That's closed today." Sometimes he uses such expressions even when it is an activity he suggested and which he enjoys. He'll ask to go to a movie, then later he'll say, "I think they're sold out" or "I don't think they're showing that movie anymore." A likely translation of these phrases might be: "I'm anxious about going to the movie theater." However, once he arrives at the movie he relaxes and enjoys himself.

Margaret, a 49-year-old fully affected adult, takes a more direct approach when anticipating an event outside her routine. She came up with several reasons why she couldn't go on a planned vacation. One was, "I can't go because my boss is going to need me." She is anxious about the trip and invented excuses express her anxiety, as well as offering logical reasons to avoid the activity. Her reasoning may be a mechanism to control anxiety, with the added bonus that it may actually prevent something from happening. Again, the activity may be something she genuinely enjoys, once she gets past the transition.

Ben surrounds his statements of things he wants to happen with a cacophony of cartoon voices and TV imitations. A great strength of those with fragile X syndrome is mimicry. They can often repeat entire cartoons, including voices and sound effects. Those who know Ben well can recognize the important sentence he is trying to communicate, hidden within a paragraph of superhero noises. One way to be indirect is to encase that anxiety-producing idea within more familiar, comfortable sounds. Sometimes he speaks in the third person. "He wants to go home, that's what he wants." This is an indirect manner of letting his parents know he wants to go home, without having to put himself at the forefront.

If Jessie wants to let me know he would just rather not go to school tomorrow—a common occurrence—the way he might put it is, "I have tennis today." I might think he was really talking about tennis, except that it is late in the evening, the time of day when his anxieties increase, and much too late for a tennis class. "Today" stands for "tomorrow" and yesterday doesn't get talked about at all. Those with fragile X exhibit a range of approaches to past, present, and future in their speech.

It's rare to get a description from Jessie of what's happened to him during the day. He has to be really excited about something or be asked just the right question to be inspired to report on daily events. Recently he did initiate an account of an exciting day. He had gone on a field trip to an animal park, and he listed the animals he had seen. I was captivated by the normalcy of the moment: my child coming home and telling me something about his day. We parents of children with disabilities love to experience "typical" behavior from our children, even when it is naughty behavior.

Alex does talk about past events, told as a familiar family tale. "Hey mom, do you remember when you burned the popcorn and had to put the bag on the porch?" He doesn't talk much about the future and what's going to happen. Instead, about 90 percent of his conversation is about these stock memories. He is also able to talk a bit about his recent interactions with people, especially those that raise strong emotions: "I walked by Michael and he stuck his tongue out at me."

Ben discusses the day to come with stock opening phrases, which his parents are expected to fill in. On weekday evenings he will start with, "On the bus...." This is the beginning of the schedule for tomorrow, when he will get "on the bus," then come home from school, and "see mom" or other family members. He is seeking reassurance that he will get home after school. On weekends he prompts his parents with a "Get up…" and they fill in the blanks. He prefers home-based activities such as "have French toast, watch TV…" and not anything having to do with making a trip outside the home. For Ben, the purpose of these lists of activities is to gain reassurance about what will be happening in his future.

Meanings of words seemed to be associated strongly with synonyms and related words. Maybe there are parallel lines of meaning running through the brain on a level that we just don't understand. Jessie, and many others with fragile X, are more easily able to access the metaphors and synonyms that run alongside the main line of meaning, than to convey the central meaning itself. I imagine it as a tight cluster of meaning, like a ball of yarn that they reach for, pulling out the loosest thread that clings lightly to the outer edges. We only hear the thread of words they can access. We have to imagine, or puzzle out, the rest of the skein. This "cluster-thinking" would be a great skill for a poet; but of course it can be a deficiency when you are trying to get across an important point.

Cluster-thinking includes opposites as well as synonyms. Such speech comes out sounding like a wire is crossed. Alex says "near" instead of "far" and on a hot day in the car, he will ask his mom to "turn the heat on." Jessie says "hot" when he means "cold" and "red" when he means "green." When he was younger, I thought perhaps he was color-blind, but then one day he matched M&Ms with a color wheel I had painted for an art class. I finally figured out that he knew he meant "red," but somewhere on the route from his brain to his mouth the word came out "green." How much time must have been wasted in elementary school when Jessie's teachers thought he didn't know his color labels! We get around it now by saying "green like grass," or "cold, icy" to make sure we understand one another.

Jessie reads in this brain-crossed, cluster-thinking way too, and it has wreaked havoc over the years with the school-testing process. He sees the word "yard" and knows what it means, but reads it aloud as "grass" or "lawn." He reads the meaning, not the letters. Alex does the same thing, looking at the word "path" and reading it as "trail." These young men have to understand the phonics (or recognize the entire word) to get the meaning, then hook that meaning up in their brains with a synonym or closely related word, which then makes its way down the neurons and comes out as spoken word. I can't think of a scientific discipline that could begin to make sense of this process; it would have to be a cross-disciplinary study.

Jessie invents his own jokes, or reworks those of others. Sometimes they make sense only to him. Some are hilarious, some are just silly.

"Why did the bird fly south for the winter?" "Because he didn't have any feet." "Knock knock." "Who's there?" "Moo." "Moo who?" "Why are you crying like an old cow?"

My stepson understands everything, except for abstract topics far outside his realm of experience. Greece probably wouldn't make sense to him as a concept, but he could certainly refer to it once he had been there or seen it in a film. He wouldn't, however, want to talk about it unless he was there, because it would imply a dreaded "transition." On the other hand, it is beyond his ability to hold a conversation that stays on topic and shows basic turn-taking skills. Nor does sequence, in general, make any sense to him. He is completely unmoved by those sets of three line drawings that first graders have to put in order of the story. This has manifested in some dyslexic-like problems with reading, which makes reading multisyllabic words especially difficult.

Educators see the ability to sequence as a prerequisite for learning other skills. I hate to think how much time was wasted holding Jessie back from being taught whatever comes next in the standard teaching sequence. Like many with fragile X, he has spotty skills that defy the typical learning sequence, and I have spent many hours urging teachers to move on to new topics and skills despite his inability to master certain "basics." Piaget might be turning over in his grave, but if so, he couldn't have known any children with fragile X.

There is one situation in which my favorite fragile X code-talker knows exactly what to say and how to behave. When someone is upset or angry, Jessie moves quickly to restore equilibrium. Never mind that he has learned this as an adaptive skill to fend off his own anxiety; it still shows a real facility for reading people and choosing the right response. Sometimes it's blatant manipulation. If I'm a little grouchy I get a big smackaroo on the cheek and a crushing hug. He'll serve me a wine glass filled with sparkling cider, and distract me with a joke from his teddy bear—who speaks in a unique voice with a set of particularly silly phrases—or a bowl of microwave popcorn.

One summer, when Jessie was about 14, a college-age counselor at a regular teen day camp let me know that she recognized Jessie's talent for making people feel better. "Jessie is very empathetic," she told me. A girl in the camp had been upset and crying, and Jessie sat right next to her and talked with her soothingly. "I didn't know what to say to her, and Jessie knew right away," the counselor told me. I got tears in my eyes and thanked her for telling me. It is so seldom that Jessie is seen as a skilled person with his own unique talents, although to my eye, he has many. I was deeply moved that someone outside the family had understood something important about him. So few people take the time to really know our children as human beings, rather than just as people with a disability. Many of our children have unique talents, such as in art, cooking, music, or making people feel at home. It's as important to nurture these specific skills and abilities as it is to work on life skills, math, and reading.

I wish I could send that camp counselor over to explain all this to the department store checker who, when she saw me in line with Jessie, turned to me and said, "God bless you," in a pitying voice. Well, yes, He has. Thank you for noticing. I am blessed to have in my life this friendly, funny, poetic young man who has challenged me to understand him and learn from him. He may have presented me with a set of new issues and problems, but at the same time I get to listen to and puzzle over the wonderful, meaningful clusters of ideas that make up his fragile X code-talk. I laugh a lot more than I would have without him. I have a deeper understanding of metaphor, and how one word can carry a wealth of meaning.

Expectations

Randy Weaver, the father of three, has one child who is a carrier of fragile X and one who has the full mutation.

As fathers, we all have expectations for our children. We have expectations as to who they will become, whether they will go to college, what they will do for their profession, when they will get married and have kids and make us grandfathers. When you discover that your child has a disability, those expectations can change quickly. Some may have a difficult time letting go of the previous expectations, some may let go too quickly and give up all expectations. Most of us will fall somewhere in between.

My middle son was diagnosed at age 3 with fragile X syndrome. Prior to that time, our family struggled with concerns about his physical and mental development. Several misdiagnoses later, we had the answer to the question of why he acted this way and why he was not falling in line with our "expectations." Shortly after the diagnosis, my wife visited a local family who had a teenage son with fragile X syndrome. She came back from that visit devastated. She got a glimpse into what the future held for us, and she had a hard time as she let go of her previous expectations for our son. That family has two boys with fragile

X. The youngest is higher functioning than the oldest. When I later went to visit them with her, I found the oldest boy was employed but living at home and the youngest was a very happy and funny teenager. Both were obviously very much loved and supported by their parents and their siblings. My reaction was not one of despair as we discussed the other family's expectations for their kids and thought about ours. At the time I didn't understand why I wasn't more affected by that glimpse of the future.

In the years to follow, led by my amazing wife, we have pushed our son—and ourselves, for that matter—into situations well outside our comfort zone. We have made a conscious effort to expose him to the "real world" as much as possible. The payoffs have been unbelievable. He's one of the most popular kids at his school. He's played football on the school team and scored four touchdowns, thanks to a creative coaching staff. He spent a week at camp with a non-disabled friend, he's gone on church mission trips and learned to use power tools, he integrated into the mainstream classes at his school in a district that, until now, did not see the benefits of inclusion. It's not to say that all these experiences are for everyone, but it is to say that because of my wife's courage to push the envelope (yes, she gets the credit), these opportunities for him to thrive (as well as fail) have presented themselves readily.

To be honest, I hadn't put a lot of thought into what my expectations really were for my kids. I had some basic and typical ones for my oldest daughter and youngest son: they will go to college, get married, make me a grandpa, et cetera. For my middle son, however, it was a different story, especially following his diagnosis with fragile X. My best friend asked me one day about a year ago, "What are your expectations for Zach?" My answer surprised both him and me. I said, "I don't have any." That sounded a bit weird even to me; but then I immediately followed by saying, "I don't have any because he has never shown me what he can't do. He's only showed me what he can do." I found that every time I let go of my preconceived notions as to how a situation should turn out, I am pleasantly surprised by both my son's performance and enjoyment, as well as the love and support that friends and even strangers have shown towards him.

In a similar fashion, I noticed one expectation I've always held. I have always had a somewhat naïve belief that all people are basically kind and not always looking out for only themselves. The world often has the opposite expectation and we have run into that paradox many times with our son. A great example is when we pushed very hard for an inclusive school environment in elementary school. Statements were made, noting that this may work in elementary school, but the kids in middle school will not be so accommodating and will be cruel. As validated by the successes we've seen, my expectation about people has proved correct. Zach has thrived at every new stage and it has as much, and perhaps even more, to do with the love and support he receives from all those he interacts with than it does with him and his abilities. I'm starting to think I may not be so naïve.

Looking back on what our expectations were and what they are now, it makes me realize how important it has been that we have not put boundaries around what we think Zach can do. It is a much richer life to have him show us where the boundaries are and not let ourselves define them for him. The same holds true for our other children and for ourselves. That's something I struggle to keep in view as I approach new situations and try new things. It takes an immense amount of courage and trust to step outside your comfort zone and that's why I respect my son more than anyone else on this earth.

Whether your child is "normal" or disabled, short, tall, thin, overweight, pierced, spiked hair or clean cut—whatever—let them show you what they can do. When you are there to catch them when they fall—and they will—they can move forward without fear to do things, be the kind of person to affect the lives of others in a positive way, far beyond what you may ever have expected.

Holding Up, Letting Go

Nancy Abrams, an award-winning author and photojournalist, is the mother of two sons with fragile X syndrome.

My son Simon began preparing me for his transition from child to adult long ago. He was 6 years old and had just been diagnosed with fragile X syndrome. His older brother Sam had abandoned his old two-wheeler for a larger bike, and Simon wanted the old bike. He didn't know how to ride a two-wheeler, and I didn't believe he was ready to learn. I didn't think he was able. I tried to explain that to him, but he shut his eyes, shook his head, and stuck out his lower lip. I suggested training wheels, but Simon just said, "No!"

I sat on my front porch and watched him struggle with the bike. It was the perfect size. Simon could sit on the seat and still have both feet on the ground. All day long he practiced, lifting one foot, then the other, learning to balance. The wheels lurched forward. Sometimes he slowly fell over.

He wasn't having any fun. But he persisted.

And then the magic moment happened. Simultaneously he pedaled and balanced. He was off down the street. His smile was triumphant.

128

I got to my feet and applauded. I was so proud. And then I realized he was riding away from me…fast.

I ran after him.

And I've been running ever since.

This is the truth about transition: It is letting go. It is watching your child struggle to get away from you, to realize his own future.

When most parents consider their children's options after high school, they visit campuses. When I took Simon on this rite-of-passage trip, no ivy-covered walls greeted us. Instead, we found ourselves in depressing neighborhoods, in buildings that felt like factories.

We visited vocational centers, peeked into rooms filled with long stretches of tables, and watched workers with Down syndrome, autism, and who-knows-what-diagnosis put together tops for bubble bath bottles, seal unidentifiable parts in plastic bags, and wrap multipacks of dog food. We also observed building maintenance students wrestle floor buffers, and we walked by four men using machines to press metal pieces into useful shapes. I scanned faces, looking for fragile X syndrome.

At one center, clients' aptitudes were defined by what floor they worked on: lower floor, lower abilities; higher floor, higher abilities. When our guide and Simon and I walked into a room, faces turned toward us. Sometimes we drew a smile or a wave. Simon pulled his hat down until it nearly covered his eyes and dug his hands deeper into his pockets, signs that he was uncomfortable. I masked my feelings. "Nice," I told our guide.

I couldn't picture Simon doing "factory work." Yes, I recognize his limitations: he can't read; math might as well be Greek. In spite of 15 years of speech therapy, his verbal communication skills are poor. His mouth refuses to form certain sounds. He talks fast and he talks all the time. He perseverates on a topic: Christine Aguilera, NASCAR, movies, history. Out of the blue will come a sentence like, "Abraham Lincoln was shot at the movies."

"The theater," I automatically reply.

But Simon has real strengths. He loves to work, to use his muscles. He has a natural affinity for art. He is funny and kind. His red hair and bright blue eyes lend a special charm. He has a real gift for making people feel good about themselves.

When Simon graduated from high school, I thought his transition into the real world would go smoothly. He had worked throughout the school year at a local car repair shop, and they offered him a job. But in the fall Simon's boss became too busy to supervise Simon's work. Simon's hours were cut back, and by New Year's he was not working at all.

"Simon needs a prevocational evaluation," said a counselor at the Division of Vocational Rehabilitation. He gave us a list of vocational centers and we decided to visit three. I wish I could say our decision was based on reputation. But *U.S. News and World Report* doesn't rank these centers. I looked at a map and tried to pick places that didn't pose serious transportation challenges.

At the center we liked best, the walls were covered with murals of colonial times, people working in fields, at commerce. Our guide explained that the building formerly belonged to Colonial Insurance Company. The art felt oddly appropriate. And the center was close to a train station.

When the counselor asked me how Simon would get to the center, I didn't hesitate.

"The train," I said.

"Can he do that on his own?" she asked.

"Yes," I answered immediately, before doubt could shake my voice. "We'll practice."

Simon and I made our first trip late in March, boarding the train on a cold, sunny day. When the conductor came by to take our tickets, she warned us that only the first four cars stopped at our destination. Panic danced in my chest. Another challenge.

"Do you understand that, Simon?" I asked.

"Yes," he said, drawing out the syllable to let me know that the question irritated him.

Simon kept up a steady stream of chatter, talking about his basketball team's victory in the Special Olympics, telling me he likes my sisters better than he likes me. He pulled his ball cap low over his eyes. I stared out the window, watching as prosperous suburbs gave way to shabby homes, littered roads, and abandoned lots.

Our destination, a once-beautiful station tarnished by decay, was being renovated. We made our way around blocked pathways, down a stairway that smelled of urine.

"Pew. It stinks!" Simon said.

We found ourselves facing a grocery store. I looked for the best route around it, but either side led through a parking lot.

"Watch for cars," I warned Simon.

I led Simon to a crosswalk, pointed out the big red brick church across the street.

"Remember that," I said. "And always cross at the light."

Simon understands the white-light walking man. But the next intersection just flashed a walk/don't walk signal. Another flutter of fear.

"Simon, you understand red lights, green lights, right?" I asked.

Again, the drawn-out yes.

We walked by lots bordered by chain-link fences, tall apartment buildings, and a gas station that sold a brand of cheap cigarettes I did not recognize. I have to admit, the neighborhood made me a little nervous. But Simon seemed unfazed. He pointed out the center.

"There it is," he said. "I found it."

We had been there twice, so I wasn't surprised that Simon recognized the building. After a brief stop inside, where Simon said hello to the security guard, we headed back to the train station.

We picked up lunch in a small restaurant, shouting our orders over loud Spanish music. "This is great," Simon said. He loved the new experience. When it was time to catch the train, I made sure that Simon knew which side was westbound and we headed home.

On his first day at the center, I accompanied Simon on his trip, trying to be hands-off, watching as he made the traveling decisions, shadowing his movements.

It was raining and we each held an umbrella as we skirted the deeper puddles. Simon walked quickly, in front of me, and I followed. I tried to keep the nervous mother inside of me quiet as Simon waited for the lights to change and safely crossed the street. Every once in a while he'd turn and say, "You coming?" I could tell he was irked by my slow pace. He had no trouble finding the center and hurried inside without a wave good-bye. I turned around and retraced my steps to the train.

The first time Simon climbed aboard the Midtown Express in Millburn by himself, he didn't even turn to wave. I had to fight the urge to jump on the train after him. Instead, I rushed to the nearest conductor.

"My son has disabilities and he just got on the train," I said. The conductor just looked at me.

"Simon has bright red hair and it's hard to understand his speech," I rattled on. The conductor had one hand on the rail. It was all-aboard time.

The train rumbled off. I plodded to my car, trying to breathe normally. I resisted my immediate urge to call Simon's cell phone.

I drove home from the station, heart pounding, fighting the "bad mother" refrain in my head. It's not the first time that song has haunted me.

He'll call me when he gets to school, I thought.

He didn't.

And I didn't call him either.

Now, every morning, Simon joins the well-dressed businessmen and women at the local station. When the train pulls in, Simon rushes away.

And he will always be heading away from me. I just have to learn to balance the holding up and the letting go. For years I have prayed for just a little glimpse of normal. So here it is: Like all parents, I must relinquish my child to the world.

The Itsy Bitsy Spider

Roberta Oberman is the mother of a son with the full mutation of fragile X syndrome.

From the beginning of our story about Eric, the nursery song "The Itsy Bitsy Spider" was my anthem. For those of you who don't know this little song, you will have to make up your own music to go with the words. It goes something like this: "The Itsy Bitsy Spider went up the water spout, down came the rain and washed the spider out, out came the sun and dried up all the rain—and The Itsy Bitsy Spider went up the drain again." I would gain a little bit of knowledge, a little bit of patience, a little bit of headway, and then just as swiftly, the "rain" would pour down on me and I would go back to square one.

Eric was born on November 25, 1975. From the beginning he was baffling. I spent Thanksgiving in the hospital, endured a horrible turkey dinner, and gave birth during *Monday Night Football*. Neither the doctor nor my husband was too pleased about Eric's timing. His birth was fairly easy, except that he presented "sunny-side up." Because of this, his face and nose were a bit shmooshed. He was a small baby who appeared to have a slight case of jaundice. Other than that we assumed he was a normal baby boy and we couldn't wait to enjoy him.

A week after we brought him home and as soon as the nurse left, Eric's crying began. I never heard a peep until the nurse left. Eric cried and screamed and fussed and never napped. He had to be held constantly from the very start and the horrible noisy swing that saved our sanity never stopped. Crank, Crank, Crank. It was certainly not quiet and smooth like the ones manufactured today. I was so exhausted that I had to sleep any time he did, even if it was for 20 minutes at a time, no matter what time of day. I therefore never ate a full meal and ironically it was the best diet I ever encountered. It was pretty clear that something was not right. Eric's first pediatrician told me when he was about 3 months old that he seemed "floppy." I had no idea what this meant so I ran to the bookstore to get my first of many books on early childhood development.

We switched to a soy-based formula and then to Nutramagen. This was awful stuff that had to be made from a powder. The doctor thought he must be allergic to both the regular and soy formula; I thought he was allergic to everything. Every time he had an abnormal stool or cried out in the night, I thought it was the food he had eaten during the day. On many nights, two hours after he was put down for the night the screaming would begin. Every night became a "cry watch." Sometimes I would sleep on the floor of his room after these episodes just not to have to get up out of bed again. The Itsy Bitsy Spider began to rear its "ugly little head." One day would be good, and the next three would be bad. The rain was continually pouring.

I was cranky and scared, but smart enough to know something was not right. By the time Eric was 4 months old I didn't just think it. I *knew* he was not developing normally. He did not put things in his mouth. I know it might seem strange to most people that I should notice this, but all babies put everything in their mouths. Eric did not. His floppiness, as I learned, meant that his muscles were not as strong as they should be. He did not use his pincher grasp, although he did pick up Cheerios with his thumb and middle finger. All these behaviors strung together, along with his not being able to amuse himself for more than 1 minute, led me to believe I was right. Entertaining and playing by himself was something he did not do at this early age or as a toddler. He always needed me to hold him or stimulate him by feeding him, wheeling him in the stroller, or taking him for a ride in the car. I went to the mall every day just to get out of the house and taking him to the doctor made for a thrilling field trip. He was quiet in the car, but I always feared he would fall asleep for just a minute and the afternoon nap would be ruined. I would have my own meltdown when he fell asleep in the car because I knew I would have no rest at all for the remainder of the day. It wasn't his fault, but I couldn't help but want to cry and scream at him. All these behaviors combined made me confident that what I believed was the truth, which freaked me out. I was so scared I would be right, but I prayed I would be wrong. I begged and cried that nothing would be wrong with my child. But that gut instinct we all have set to work; I was very frightened. The clouds kept on forming over me.

I continued going to the same pediatrician, who was not much help. He had no answers and kept telling me that Eric seemed okay to him. Eric was puzzling, because although he accomplished most of the developmental milestones, he performed them just a bit slower than the average baby. Although it became apparent that his large muscle control was affected, he turned over and sat up by himself appropriately at the "normal" stage; he did not crawl until he was 13 months old and didn't walk until 15 months. It was too late for crawling, and then too fast to start walking. He had limited eye contact and was definitely not cuddly. I was absolutely nuts by then and couldn't stop reading books about child development. Remember that at the time there were no computers or Internet. I had access to very limited information. My husband was completely supportive, but also not home all day. He was trying desperately to make a living for us and then would come home to a strung-out, depressed, exhausted, and angry wife. I am eternally grateful for his love for our family. It helped me survive.

When Eric was 18 months old, I finally accepted that we needed to take him to a neurologist. His pediatrician could not give us definitive answers to any of our questions. I had to find out anything I could at this point. After hours of testing we discovered that Eric might be learning disabled. Well, finally someone believed me. The neurologist told us that Eric might be retarded—or he might not be retarded. The rain just kept on pouring, and that little spider kept being washed down the drain. Every time this happened to me, I thought I would not be able to go on. I was told via telephone by the pediatrician that I would have to find proper schooling so that Eric would be able to be part of society. I thought, "What is happening? This must be a nightmare. How could this doctor talk like this about my child?" I was also encouraged to have an electroencephalogram—an EEG—done on Eric. Although I was petrified, I relented. This was one of the most excruciating and horrible experiences I have ever had to go through. I was forced to listen to my baby screaming from behind closed doors while he was being prepped to be put to sleep for the EEG. How stupid I was not to take Eric and walk out when they told me that I could not stay with him in the room. I could have rocked him to sleep better than let him scream to sleep. This kind of incident would not be tolerated today. And in the end, the results showed nothing.

I went to many, many doctors after this. I won't bore you with those details, but most of them did not really listen and were too busy to be concerned with my child. I had only one friend in Philadelphia and no family in the area. The babies and moms with whom we came into contact did not really want to be with us. Eric was fussy and their darlings were brilliant. I had no patience or time for idle talk anyway. So I went to the doctors, hospitals, therapy, and the rest by myself. My husband could only attend on his day off. I learned to be self-reliant, and probably a bit hardened. Eric was put on medication, which was a difficult decision for sure. We tried so many different drugs over the years, from stimulants to powerful tranquilizers to antidepressants. Some took weeks to work, others were unfit for him immediately; none of the early ones helped the situation or his behavior. Being drugged for Little League baseball was not a good thing. The ball would zoom by his little head and he wouldn't even notice. We had to pull him out for fear he would be hit in the head with a baseball. Guilt and shame took over and all I could think was, "What am I doing to this child by drugging him?" The only valuable information this doctor related to me was, "If your child was a diabetic, would you hold back giving him insulin?" I emphatically said "NO!" and therefore had no choice. If medicating my child would help him, my husband, my daughter, and me, then there was no choice—we had to keep trying. Scheduling pills became a daily routine. And as time passed, Eric became so good at taking them he could swallow pills anywhere without water. We called this "magic." I would give him his pills and then say, "Eric, do your magic." Never once did he let me down.

Nursery-school teachers could not figure out what was wrong with Eric. He could read, play, and was sweet, and yet he would bop a child over the head for no reason at all. He would also impulsively hug his playmates a bit too hard. He would have temper tantrums when I would pick him up at school to go home; the teachers could barely get him in my car. At the time, no one could figure this out. I now believe he was so stimulated by my car pulling up to the line, that he had a meltdown until he was finally able to get in. Once in he settled right down. I was once accused of child abuse by his nursery-school teacher when he had fallen off a bench at a friend's house and went to school the next day with a black eye. They must have figured that they now knew why he would flip out when I picked him up. Fortunately, I had many witnesses to the fall. I can't even imagine the ramifications if I hadn't had people to back me up. I just became more depressed and sad; the guilt was almost unbearable to endure. Eric was incredibly hard to care for, but I loved him with all of my heart. But I was angry at him too, angry at me, at God, at anyone I could blame. I always donated to the March of Dimes before I became pregnant, so how could this happen to me?

Of course not all was bad, as Eric loved to watch cars and traffic. We would sit on a grassy hill and watch the cars, and I am sure this is how he learned his colors. This activity kept his attention for a good 20 minutes. Spinning plastic donuts was one of his favorite things to do, and because he did this so well, you would have thought he had great small-muscle control. We now know that spinning is an autistic behavior. He also loved to watch Mr. Rogers and *Sesame Street.* How thankful I was for a little bit of time to cook dinner or make my phone calls.

During the next few years I tried to get pregnant again. It took me 2 years to conceive my daughter, Suzanne. My children are 5 years apart and best friends. God knew what he was doing to prevent me from getting pregnant again too soon. Suzanne is 24 years old and Eric is now 29. Suzanne has been tested twice for fragile X and so far the tests conclude that she is not a carrier. Obviously throughout the pregnancy I was frightened for the baby I was carrying. Not until a crystal candlestick exploded a few nights before her delivery did I stop worrying. My mother said it was a sign and the baby would be fine. We both cried.

Suzanne has been a joy to her brother and to us since the day she was born. She will always be her brother's advocate and closest friend. Ironically, by the time Suzanne was 1 year old, Eric would hit her, steal toys from her, and impulsively do naughty things. She seemed to understand even then that her brother meant no harm. She knew I had no control over his actions, my screaming meant nothing, and the phrase "time out" was meaningless. He always apologized and hugged her afterwards and she always forgave him. By the time Suzanne was 2 years old, we had explained to her many times about how different and special both she and her brother were. She understood very early what her role in the dynamics of our family would be. Both of my children were so different from one another that they were both treated like only children. Therefore never was there one "itsy bitsy" bit of jealousy.

Eric went to private school for kindergarten. It was a learning year for all of us. We went to conferences and realized just how much one-on-one attention he actually needed—a lot! I had a tremendous amount of learning to do to prepare myself and Eric for the move to public school for first grade. The strange thing was, Eric had no trouble with the transition to different schools. He never missed a day, and was always happy to go.

Our very first experience with the public school system had to do with transportation. Our neighborhood was brand-new and this was the first year for school buses. We were notified that the bus would not come into our neighborhood, but would stop one half-mile down the road on the corner of a main intersection with a busy, heavily traveled street. This was my first endeavor fighting bureaucracy issues with the government. I called the transportation department and asked what I needed to do to get this changed. I was told to write a petition to have any chance for change. I not only wrote it, but I went door-to-door to neighbors I had never met. I pleaded with everyone to sign the petition, and in the end it worked. The bus stop was two doors down from my house from then on. I succeeded and it felt good, but that was only the beginning of my career as Eric's advocate. Eric was spared some highly stressed moments, and I got my foot into the door of the "system." Somehow I had to "get through the rain."

First grade was a year of acceptance for us. His teacher told us he could not stay in a regular classroom the following year. He would suffer due to lack of attention and ridicule from other children in the class, and this would prove to be deadly. More disappointments, more tears, more praying. Special schooling, occupational therapy, speech therapy, music lessons, karate lessons, swimming lessons. We learned what was meant by an Individual Education Plan—an IEP. There were bad teachers, mean kids, doctors, and more doctors. This became our reality. My entire life became focused on finding out more and more to help Eric. I became an expert about the laws for the disabled and networked every day. I learned how to handle teachers, principals, tutors, doctors, psychologists, and babysitters. Everyone who was in contact with Eric also had contact with me. I became an expert at buying holiday gifts for the people who were important to Eric. I learned the art of bribing, being educated, and working the system. I needed to. Eric's life depended on it. I also found out very quickly that his teachers loved to write me notes with ☹ (frowning faces) every Friday. It was the perfect way to depress us and ruin our weekend. I eventually was brave enough to tell them to write it on the following Monday so that we had a whole week to try to improve the behavior. Eric was funny, smart, sweet, and willing to please. He just needed an inordinate amount of attention that no one could really give him. The rain was starting to come in monsoons.

I eventually went to a psychologist to learn how to deal with my anger and guilt. It helped me realize that it wasn't Eric I hated. This was a big relief to me. Guilt can only hurt us. I realized that I must have had learning disabilities as a child also. Math was torture for me; I was shy and I wasn't athletic. I had trouble remembering dates for history and could not relate to geometry. Anything I couldn't relate to something else—like numbers—I could not remember. Foreign language was totally foreign, and if it did not mimic English I could not retain it. School was a hard place for me to be. Of course, back in the 1950s no one knew about learning disabilities. My parents were told that I just didn't try hard enough.

I knew in my heart that Eric got his handicap from me, and I was devastated by that. My husband was my sole advocate; he consoled me as much as he could. I tried to share my fears with family members. I thought they would care but I was wrong. I was even blamed for upsetting them. Consequently, I cried alone most of the time. The skies were full of lightening and thunderstorms, the spider was scared.

Eric had many autistic tendencies. For example; he bit his finger until it was twice its normal size and completely callused. He flapped his arms as if he was about to take off like a bird. He has not let anyone sing "Happy Birthday" to him since the age of 4. He was negative even when we knew he wanted to do what we were suggesting (i.e., go out to dinner or a movie). He would collapse on the floor when neighbors came by. He hated tags in his clothing, and any stimulation became too much for him. All these behaviors were challenges to figure out since he could not verbalize why he acted this way. I had to become a detective, trying to uncover why he was freaking out. He hated magic shows, amusement parks, and the circus, everything that we wanted to show him to expand his horizons. We could not please him and were bewildered beyond anyone's imagination.

His language was not good. He did not enunciate *R*s at all. His speech was slurred and he spoke very quickly. I had to interpret everything he said, which was not a good thing to do. There were so many behaviors that we just could not fathom, such as face grimacing. I would say, "Eric don't make those faces." He would reply, "What faces?" I would go into his bedroom at 5 a.m. to try to get him to stop making strange noises for fear he would wake up his sister. I literally begged and pleaded sweetly in a soft voice and wept for him to stop. He denied making any noises. I would just shake my head in disbelief, and as soon as I left the room, the airplane noises would start again. At this point, I really had no understanding of what was going on in my child's mind.

I did not find a doctor to believe me until, believe it or not, Eric was 7 years old. I will always say that this doctor saved my life. He was a wonderful pediatrician who really listened to me and to Eric. Wow! It took only 7 years to find him. He saved us all. Never let anyone tell you that the small things you do for someone or say to someone might not change their life. All he did was listen and care. Never give up, no matter how much rain wipes that spider out because he will always climb up that spout again! Believe me, I wanted to give up so many times. I always felt as if I were at the end of my rope, the end of the road, the end of the world. There were no more tears left to cry.

We were now on to a new set of doctors. We were seeing a neurologist—which I was opposed to, since I didn't have a favorable opinion of the first one years before—and a psychiatrist. It took 2 years for me to get up the courage to go to see both of these doctors. It produced more pain by having to go through the hell of reliving Eric's history. Going to the appointments, having to wait for hours with a fidgety, cranky child, and finally enduring the demoralization and angst of their diagnosis: these things were brutal. Whenever I would hear a doctor patiently and boringly explain to us once again that our child was not normal, it was literally as if it were for the first time. A pain in my heart and my stomach occurred without fail. I did not want to do this anymore and I hoped against hope that the rain would stop. I pleaded, "Rain, rain, go away."

We suffered, and endured. The neurologist we were sent to by our pediatrician was a godsend. The psychiatrist, on the other hand, was a complete waste. He tied his shoes several times while we were explaining Eric and his behaviors. This doctor seemed bored. We saw him for 4 months and gained nothing. The doctor was not too keen on listening to us since Eric did not have emotional problems. But he certainly had eating and behavioral problems. We went to this doctor to try to get a handle on the eating issue. Eric was so thin we had to have him tested for malnourishment. He still is not a big eater today, and a very picky one at that. Many of the medications took away his appetite. It drove me absolutely crazy with worry, so for many years I made separate meals for Eric.

We were still perplexed by Eric. My prayers for answers were still coming and we hoped the new neurologist could help. This doctor was kind. He watched and listened to Eric and to us. For once I was glad that Eric displayed all his tics, grimaces, et cetera, during the visit. The doctor diagnosed Eric that day. He had what was thought of as a tic disorder with autistic tendencies, as well as ADD. He called it "tourettism," a form of Tourette syndrome. We prayed to let this be the answer. By this time we wanted to know the correct diagnosis, accept Eric's condition, and treat him appropriately. Now we at least had something new and different to probe.

Eric was once again prescribed a different medication. I went back to the library for books about Tourette syndrome. A brand new search had begun. At long last we were on a road to somewhere, although we had no idea to where. But we had some facts so we could do research. I had a little bit of hope. The sunshine was finally appearing behind the clouds. Maybe it wouldn't rain for just a little while?

Years passed. Eric's school was changed. This of course meant new friends, new teachers, and new buses. There were also different medications and new therapies. It was a whirlwind of change. Trying to remember what medication he was taking and where he was supposed to be, was a task.

It was decided that Eric would not go into the middle school of the public school system. I thought the changing of classrooms, the hall noise, cafeteria confusion, et cetera, would send him up the wall. He had made some friends and I was unhappy to have him change schools and possibly lose these few that he had. But the change was necessary. I really don't think I would have been able to endure the stress of him being in a big middle school. I still feel very strongly about inclusion and think it may be a good learning tool, but it would have been an emotional disaster that my child would never have been able to get over. Learning math, history, and biology were not high on my list of what I felt Eric needed for his survival in this world. He was enrolled through the public school system in the Vanguard School. We now had a whole new set of problems, including transportation, because this school was a good distance from our home.

These next years were different than the early ones. For the most part, Eric was on the road to becoming an adult. We arranged a private bar mitzvah for him and had a party that was sure to be low-key. Eric would not have been able to handle a full congregation watching him. I was always so anxious about his behavior and what he was going to do. It turned out to be a wonderful day, but emotional as well. As Eric was being blessed by the rabbi, I of course cried my eyes out. We had a small party for friends and family who had touched Eric's life in some way. There was not one person there who did not know him and care for him.

One plain, ordinary day in 1990 the pediatrician called me. He said, "Robbie, I'd like you to bring Eric in for a blood test for fragile X syndrome." Eric was 15 years old before we heard of fragile X. Not surprisingly, I was shocked and questioned the doctor about this strangely named syndrome. He told me he did not know too much about it himself. But we had Eric tested and the rest is history. I turned out to be the carrier, as I had previously believed. There was more rain and many tears. The "Itsy Bitsy Spider" was washed out for days, but there was relief as well. Eric was one of only a few to be diagnosed with fragile X at that time. There were no Web sites and very little information to be found.

Eric switched schools again due to a change in the population of the Vanguard School. He attended the Pathway School until he graduated at age 21 with a high school diploma. Our whole family was extremely proud of him. He had many friends, the teachers loved him, and he learned. He could not count money, but he could tell you all kinds of trivia about sports, music, history, news, celebrities, television, et cetera. He was only allowed to watch *Good Morning America* before school in the mornings; and he learned from watching *Wheel of Fortune* at dinnertime. I fought with my husband about this for years. I wanted quiet time at dinner, but he and the kids wanted *Jeopardy!* They were correct; it was the right thing for Eric. I swear he learned more from these shows than from school. He was and is a quiz-show whiz.

At this point in this essay, I could go on and on about the next 14 years, but there is no room. Eric's medication is stabilized. He has worked, had job coaches, trained, and gone to school. He has learned an amazing amount in his lifetime, and he is a success. He worked for 6 years at Whole Foods Market in Philadelphia, and I was his job coach there when he started. He currently works at Publix Supermarket in Boca Raton, Florida. His sister lives and works nearby. My husband and I have relocated to Delray Beach, Florida, for 8 months of every year. My husband practices dentistry in Pennsylvania and travels back and forth during the winter months. We plan to be living in Florida full time within the next few years.

We took extra "care" of our marriage by going on vacation often while Eric was growing up—but not without extreme anxiety. Babysitters became a priority and I searched far and wide. I needed to go somewhere to mourn and to come alive again. The kids were not thrilled with some of my babysitting choices, but in the long run it worked and it gave them a break from us as well.

There has been so much joy and heartache. Eric has turned out to be the sunshine in our world, and his sister, the blue sky. He now lives with his roommate in an apartment at the Jewish Association for

145

Residential Citizens in Boca Raton. Eric has matured amazingly over the years. He takes care of himself and works 4 days a week. He cooks, cleans (not well, but who cares), shops, and goes out to dinner and to the movies with friends. He has a credit card, which is invaluable since he still has great difficulty with money. With the help of his coach, he pays his bills, goes to the bank, and buys his beloved video games. His coach is wonderful and helps Eric achieve success. He has a cell phone (which he forgets to take with him sometimes) and he takes a computer lesson once a week. He is happy and we are too. My friends look for him at the supermarket and love to "kibitz" with him. How different the world is when we all grow up!

I am completely open about fragile X and do indeed explain it to those who are unfamiliar with the disorder. People aren't as embarrassed to hear about it as they used to be. There was a time when I would speak of Eric's medical condition just to see how these perfect mothers with their perfect children would react. Most could not even look at me. Now, most people will actually listen without feeling uncomfortable. They all tell me how wonderful it is that I "let" Eric go. That seems preposterous to me, as this has been my life's work. My goal in life was to be able to help Eric be as independent and successful as possible. Isn't that what all parents want for all their children?

When you read about all the achievements of other children and they seem to be outstanding and far better than your own, don't despair. I read stories in the *Fragile X Quarterly*, and would think to myself, why isn't there anything special about Eric? Sports, music, cooking, community work, anything? But, now I realize, he is ever so SPECIAL. A parent once exclaimed about her developmentally handicapped son, "He can do better than be a bagger at the supermarket." Eric was working as a bagger at Whole Foods Market when she said this. I was taken aback. I felt sad for her. I was happy that Eric was happy and successful, that's all. Eric loves to talk to all his customers. He could not sit at a computer, or do piecework. For him, working at the supermarket is perfect. Yes, want the best, but don't squash your child in the process.

Never, ever in a zillion years would I have thought Eric would be the person he is today. No, he is not a college graduate, and neither am I, so who cares? Some of the greatest satisfaction today comes from the simple things. Eric will now let me hug him and give him a kiss on the cheek. He lets me say, "I love you." When he sees either his dad or me walk into Publix, he no longer starts talking to himself. He has stopped getting so agitated when he's caught off guard. He has learned to compensate.

Never let anyone keep you from fighting for what you feel you can accomplish, even if it's pouring rain.

A Grandmother's Story

Leonie Star is a freelance writer who recently served as the president of the Fragile X Association of Australia.

I have knowingly been a fragile X grandmother since 1996, when my much beloved James, my first grandchild, was diagnosed with fragile X syndrome. It is a label I wear with pride. I have been asked several times to write a book or even a magazine article about my experiences. Although I am a writer, the mere thought of doing this seemed so confronting that I always declined. Nevertheless, when a few years ago I was asked by the newsletter editor of a scholarly organization to which I belong to write a piece for their journal, I agreed. Before James's diagnosis I would have written about legal jurisprudence, the Family Court of Australia, or an aspect of medieval Jewish history. Finally, I thought, I would be brave. I wrote a very short article, which I hoped would raise the consciousness of members of that organization to nonacademic issues which to some people are of vital importance. As those affected by fragile X often carry their burden of sorrow silently when in the company of those whose family members fit into the "regular" category, I felt that a bit of consciousness-raising would be timely. The article was later republished in the newsletter of the Fragile X Association of Australia and what appears here is a much enlarged version of it.

I hesitated for so long because I knew that putting pen (or computer) to paper would rake up a lot of submerged sorrow, not only mine but that of my close family members as well. For me to write honestly about this situation would be extremely difficult. My hesitation was also caused in part because it was not only my story I was telling. As anyone who has disability in the family knows, each family member is intimately involved and the ramifications of a diagnosis of a genetic syndrome can be life-altering. I now think I can finally speak for myself and my own reactions but do not want to trespass on the feelings of others. Both my children—Naomi, mother of James, and Adrienne, her younger sister—have read this article and were offered the opportunity to make changes. However, what is written here is basically my own account, which I have made as accurate and open as I can.

Longing for grandchildren as I had always done, I had wondered how best to perform this role. A wise friend told me to keep my ears open and my mouth shut (a bit difficult for me); to this I added nonjudgmental love, endless support, and being available at all times— which is OK when you are all in the same city but impossible when separated by an ocean. I recognize that grandparents of children with a disability are in an especially difficult position. In our case, added to the usual restrictions I placed upon myself (particularly the "mouth shut" one) was the knowledge that very soon Naomi knew almost everything there was to know about fragile X while I knew almost nothing. My ignorance meant that the fear of intruding became far more significant. However, I have never found anything to criticize in the way Naomi and her husband, Chad, have raised James. If you favor the view that children pick their parents, James chose his brilliantly: Naomi and Chad are the ideal parents for a child with a disability. They display endless patience and commitment, together with an attitude which sees the glass as half full rather than half empty. They meet James's needs in every way from a perspective which is informed and practical, as well as loving.

149

I am not only a fragile X grandmother but a *Jewish* fragile X grandmother. In a brilliant book entitled *Haikus for Jews* by David M. Bader, there is a telling question: "Is one Nobel Prize so much to ask from a child after all I've done?" Though both academics, neither my former husband, recently deceased, nor I subscribed to the philosophy behind this poem. All either of us wanted for James and any other grandchildren we might have was that they be happy and fulfilled, which is where I think the Jewish part comes in. We both surrounded James with love. He was equally lucky with his other grandparents, as they adore him and spend much of their time assisting him in furthering his major pursuit.

Thirteen years ago, in the middle of a seemingly endless Los Angeles late summer heat wave, James was born. I was fortunate to see him within 2 hours of his birth. I remember also visiting the hospital later that day and having a long talk with him. At least, I did the talking and he seemed to listen intently, even making eye contact. I did not know then how much we would all long for this particular kind of contact in years to come. I did not talk about the usual grandparents' hopes, such as that James will grow up to become a baseball star or President of the United States. (As an Australian, I do not think this is important and we do not harbor similar feelings about our Prime Ministers.) Instead, I told him about A.A. Milne's Winnie the Pooh and recited some of that author's poems published in *When We Were Very Young.* For many years James was regularly treated to renditions of the poem "Disobedience," because the main character was "James, James, Morrison, Morrison." (I changed the ending, as Naomi was very firm about not exposing children to frightening material.) Looking back, I can't remember that he was ever even the slightest bit interested, although I got a lot of fun out of it.

By the time James was 9 months old it became obvious that he was not developing at the same rate as other children. What followed is a set of circumstances common to many families with fragile X. Naomi was never in denial and was the first to realize that something was seriously wrong. Neither Chad nor I fully agreed with her at this point, although we were aware of James's slowness. I have always believed that children develop at their own pace. Just because most children reach a milestone at a specified time, it does not mean that all children do so. However, by James's first birthday, when I went over to Los Angeles again, I could see the marked difference between his abilities and those of his playgroup peers. At one playgroup session I attended, James cried endlessly, even though Naomi carried him the whole time. In retrospect, the sensory overload for him must have been extreme. I was upset and tried to hide this; above all I wanted him to join in and enjoy himself with the other kids.

I will not go into the endless round of medical and specialist appointments that Naomi and Chad embarked upon on two continents—when James was 18 months old they moved to Sydney. In order to inject some wry humor into our common situation, in one of the Fragile X Association of Australia newsletters we published a list of "Fourteen comments you didn't need to hear from your GP, pediatrician, teacher or friend, but you always do." I think my family must have heard all of them, including, "You're a first time Mum and it's natural to be over anxious." "You have to stop comparing him to his brother/sister/friends." "All children can't be overachievers." "It's just a lag—he'll catch up." "Tell me what you think is wrong." "What's normal?" "My own son didn't sit/stand/walk/talk until he was much older than yours." "Are you a psychologist?" and, with ultimate condescension, "He's fine, but how are you coping? You seem stressed."

What I found most distressing and cruel was the comment, obviously common parlance among general practitioners, made to Naomi about James: "He's what we call an 'FLK'—a funny- looking kid." This, before diagnosis, cut me to the heart. Still all these years later, I can be reduced almost to tears and develop gut-wrenching cramps in my stomach if I hear prejudicial remarks made about James. Perhaps this type of reaction never goes away. In my case, it hardly even seems to moderate.

Specialists in Australia said that James didn't fit into "any known syndrome"—perhaps an expression of their own ignorance—while tests for several conditions proved negative, including fragile X. At that time I knew almost nothing about the syndrome, particularly about its ramifications, although it must have been mentioned in my presence. When James was about 4 years old there was a family lunch to celebrate my former mother-in-law's birthday. A sister-in-law told me that Naomi had been upset by conversations she had had with a cousin in Melbourne. I asked what it was about and was told it concerned fragile X, to which I replied blithely that James had tested negative for it.

I remember when I was given the news. It was a weekend and I was having a peaceful lunch by myself, reading the Saturday papers. Naomi and Chad came in and with some agitation told me that, because of the diagnosis of a cousin with the same genetic heritage, James had been retested and found to have fragile X. Still I did not wake up to the seriousness of the situation and this was not spelled out for me at the time. While well aware of chronic physical illness, from which I have suffered since 1980, the idea of developmental delay in our family was a new concept to me. I was aware of Down syndrome and also knew a little about autism, but I had not encountered other similar conditions. I did not realize then the steep learning curve we were all about to enter.

Everybody deals with grief differently and, as all people with fragile X in their families know, it can be a very isolating experience. Even after the initial period of mourning for the child's lost opportunities, there is little stability in most people's reactions. Emotions seem to wax and wane according to what is happening at any particular time. One difficulty in our family was that I have often been ill since James's diagnosis. To Naomi's credit and my gratitude, she did not ever want to add extra burdens to current issues about my health. During difficult periods she was helped immeasurably by her wonderfully loving and supportive husband (boy, did she choose well there!) and by Louise Gane, then working with Dr. Randi Hagerman in Denver, Colorado. Naomi and Louise had many endless Denver-to-Sydney phone conversations, which kept Naomi sane. She has not forgotten Louise's contribution to the way she has managed James's fragile X. My granddaughter, thankfully totally free of the syndrome, is called Sophia Louise.

The story of James's education is a model for what a mother who constantly acts as her child's advocate can achieve. He went from early intervention classes, where he often hung onto his teacher's leg for the whole time he was there, to inclusion in a regular class at the local primary school. The teachers at this school had little experience of special needs children before James's arrival, but in nearly all circumstances were willing to learn. The principal was amazingly supportive. Known as a person who did not relish interruptions in her office when she was extremely busy, she always made an exception when James breezed in to show her his latest artwork. Because of my daughter's advocacy and the information she imparted to all teachers who came into contact with James, his education through the 6 years of primary school was generally very good. We found, however, that some teachers, although not specifically negative in their attitude towards James, were not willing to put in the extra time needed to bring out the very best in him, particularly as he did not constantly have an aide alongside. By this time I think we were beginning to understand that it is impossible to achieve a perfect system, no matter how much effort has gone into it. But James did learn, at his own level and pace. Perhaps more importantly, he found that he loved going to school. Halfway through James's 6th year at this school, Naomi and her family moved permanently to the United States.

From his earliest years, James has been a drummer, like his father, his grandfather, and two of his uncles. On his first birthday his paternal grandparents gave him a properly constructed drum kit, sized for his age. Chad has been teaching him the elements of drumming ever since. Luckily he is a patient man, as some of the lessons lasted only one or two minutes. Nevertheless, by the age of ten James came in 7th out of 240 youngsters in an open competition with regular kids in Sydney. Since then he has made amazing progress. Again with regular students, he is the drummer for almost all the public appearances of his middle school's jazz and concert bands. He was featured in an article entitled (of course) "The Little Drummer Boy" in the National Fragile X Foundation's *Fragile X Quarterly* of December 2005. A photo of him posed in front of his drum kit under the heading "Xtraordinary Achievements" was featured on the home page of the Web site for three months. These achievements make this grandmother want to burst with pride.

During the period from diagnosis to the present, James has progressed in many other ways. One thing about him is that he will always do his best, even if occasionally he needs to be persuaded to try something new. When Naomi's family went snowtubing recently, James initially behaved in a typical fragile X manner, saying, "No, I won't. I want to go home." Naomi finally got fed up with this attitude and pushed him down the slope. He was so entranced by this new experience that he spent hours trudging up to the top so he could slide down again, to the extent that finally he had to be almost pulled into the car when it came time to leave.

James is also extremely responsible and has taken upon himself certain weekly duties that he independently performs without fail. For instance, he collects all the garbage in the house and takes it out to the bins. Without prompting, he rings his grandparents and one of his uncles, both of whom share the same garbage night, to remind them to take their bins out as well. In fact, he rings his uncle twice, as he does not trust him to comply after the first reminder. He has become relatively outgoing, participates in all family activities (especially if they involve him going somewhere alone with his father, whom he idolizes) and, because of major improvements in his speech, is usually understood by strangers. I love it when he runs into an American restaurant before the rest of us, going up to the desk and saying firmly and clearly, "Chad, party of five." What an angel.

My obvious grandmotherly pride in his achievements is legendary. Visitors to my new apartment in Sydney are subject to an agreement that they will watch the latest DVD that has been sent to me of James's newest drumming feat. Of course, visitors are also forcibly exposed to DVDs of my granddaughter, aged 6, who looks as if she will be a consummate piano player. James has been lucky in that his middle school teacher is brilliant; she has been teaching special needs students for years and has won many awards. He is happy at school and making progress academically, especially with reading. He is very independent now. Naomi found out by accident that because there is no aide to take him out of his special class to band practice, he goes alone, through a large and difficult-to-navigate school, bringing himself back and sitting down immediately to pick up on the work that he has missed. Like many people with fragile X, he has a great sense of humor and is a joy to be with. I look at his accomplishments with awe. What for us is relatively easy must for him be so difficult. He has made excellent progress and his reliability, independence, and general attitude will go far towards fitting him into some kind of employment when the time comes.

James's condition has not materially altered my life, except to broaden it. I have learned an enormous amount about both fragile X and community service over the years. Naomi became a committee member of the Fragile X Association of Australia as soon as James was diagnosed; she eventually became president. She and a truly wonderful committee worked extremely hard over the years to ensure that the association did as much as it could for fragile X families throughout the country. This was one area where I was able to help. For many years, my house was the official postal address of the association and I was also the archivist and librarian. I soon began to research aspects of the fragile X experience, which had not then been written about in an Australian context. I wrote about transition from each of our school levels to the next, on what training was available after the end of secondary school, and on how best to get a job. It gave me great pleasure to undertake this work, especially as I felt that I was really helping the cause. When Naomi moved to the United States, I took over as president of the association but unfortunately because of ill health lasted only a year in this position. Nevertheless, being true to form, I am still writing for the newsletter, pointing out things that have to be done yesterday, and generally acting like a nag. Luckily for me our great committee does not seem to mind.

But while my life has not greatly changed, Naomi's has taken a direction I believe she never envisaged. When pregnant with James she withdrew from a partially completed music degree she was undertaking, not as a drummer but as a singer. I do not think she had ever thought she would not work outside her home after she had children, but this is how it has worked out. She continues singing and for years was a member of Australia's premier choral group, the Sydney Philharmonia Choir. But basically fragile X has consumed her life. She works for it all the time. After only a few months in America, she became the president of the Fragile X Association of Southern California and is working as hard and creatively for it as she worked for its Australian equivalent. Having got into the habit of unpaid community service, she undertakes a lot of other work in this capacity as well. I feel that the satisfaction she must derive from seeing the fantastic results of her input into fragile X associations, and specifically into James's life, must recompense her for not having other experiences that might have come her way. From my point of view her life is a consummate success.

The life of my daughter Adrienne has also been affected by the medical effects of fragile X. In her early 30s she became aware of the premature ovarian failure which so often affects female fragile X carriers. In retrospect, her subsequent decision not to have children may have been fortuitous, as she no longer lives with her then long-term partner. She revels in her role as aunt and is adored by both the children. James, in particular, thinks she is the best person in the world. As I no longer subscribe to the 1980s feminist mantra that women can have it all, I look at the growth in Adrienne's professional life (she is an interior designer and college tutor) and know that her dedication to her job, and the love of the children, form for her a firm foundation for a successful and fulfilling life.

And finally, Sophia. We called James's sister "Sophie" until at the age of 6 she announced she preferred to be called by her official name. She is already showing a strong protective side where James is concerned. When I spoke firmly to him about not walking away from me while I was talking to him, his then 5-year-old sister told me equally firmly that he has fragile X. I told her I was aware of that fact but he could still stay to hear what I had to say. James, of course, was the winner in this exchange. By the time Sophia and I had finished debating what, if any, allowances should be made for the behavior of a child with a disability, he was long gone. Sophia does not realize yet that of all the family, she is likely to be the person who will spend the most years with James. We have never subscribed to the notion that regular siblings of those with a disability should be groomed to take responsibility for them. Sophia's attitude in our debate about James's behavior was totally unprompted. Nevertheless, I hope that she will always display the love, pride, and support she now shows towards him.

As a grandmother I am in the position of being able to take an overall view of our family situation. I do not think we have so much been damaged by the presence of fragile X, as it has caused the lives of some of us to take a different direction. James's condition has resulted in all the members of the family learning lessons that we may not have learned otherwise. In a family I regard as having been loving and tolerant long before fragile X, we have all learned more of these invaluable traits. As well, we have learned how to be advocates for James and for the cause of fragile X in general. This has resulted in our opening ourselves up to the world and meeting it without fear in a way that I, at least, may not have experienced had circumstances been different.

Would I have learned different lessons if we had not had fragile X in the family? No doubt, but as they may not have been as difficult, they may also not have stretched me as much as I have been stretched. Have I as a grandmother learned lessons different from those learned by the rest of my family? Perhaps not, although with age comes a softening of attitude, so that my level of compassion has been increased immeasurably.

Grandparents of children with a disability realize that our role, one generation removed from the affected individual, causes less sorrow and constant anguish than that suffered by the parents. For them there is the daily burden of coping with unusual behavior and endlessly supporting and encouraging the children through each and every new accomplishment. But the thrill of achievement, however small the step forward, is almost equal for parents and grandparents alike. Perhaps most important of all, this grandmother knows that having a special grandchild has widened her world view and softened her personality to quite an extraordinary extent. To my most darling James, who has made this happen and who gives me constant joy by his existence, I send my undying gratitude.

The Trip To Washington, DC

*Pat Tucker is the mother of six grown children, three of whom
have fragile X. She is the president of the Board of Directors for
the Fragile X Association of Washington State.*

Every 2 years the National Fragile X Foundation holds an
International Conference to bring together scientists, educators,
families, and others who are interested in fragile X syndrome. In June
of 2004, the 9th International Conference was held in Washington, DC.
I was there because I am a carrier and my husband and I have children
with fragile X.

One of the sessions I attended was a mothers' group. I arrived
late for it because a conversation I had been engaged in—one mother
talking with another mother about their children with fragile X—had
started in the previous session, continued through the break, and spilled
into the next session. The mother I was talking to had young children
and lots of questions. I have adult children and 25 years of experience.
We had entered the session strangers but a common component opened
a door and brought us together.

I slipped into the mothers' group session, trying not to draw
attention. At least thirty women were sitting in a circle, and one was

telling the others about her family and a recent cruise they had taken. There was a catch in her voice as she spoke of her sadness that her young son with fragile X didn't appreciate the cruise, particularly since it was something that they hadn't always been able to afford.

"Woman, get a grip!" I thought as I inwardly rolled my eyes. I wanted to say, "Children *without* fragile X don't appreciate things just because we can finally afford them!" What she was really saying was that her son will never appreciate a cruise or many other things she can now afford. So what? How do we as adults define what is special? Do we expect children to like everything we like?

My husband and I had brought our adult children with fragile X with us to the conference. Leading up to departure, our sons reminded us numerous times a day of their excitement about going to Washington, DC. I wondered, What do they know about Washington, DC, that's making them so excited? It was simple: We were going on a trip and they got to go. Weeks before we left, I pulled out books and showed them pictures of the U.S. Capitol, the Washington Monument, the Lincoln Memorial, the White House. While I was in meetings at the conference my husband became their tour guide. They saw in person everything they had seen in pictures—and more. The week following the conference we extended our sightseeing to include Mt. Vernon, Monticello, and Williamsburg.

A few years ago we gave Philip, one of our sons, walkie-talkies for Christmas. During Philip's lifetime we have spent the equivalent of many days looking for him. He has not necessarily been lost, in his opinion. We just couldn't find him. We had never used the walkie-talkies but we decided to take them along on this trip. They saved us many hours of searching and provided endless hours of entertainment for Philip. He was fascinated with the buttons and sounds and the communication.

One of our visits was to Arlington National Cemetery, which covers 200 acres. Philip was not too excited about being there but I knew he would enjoy the changing of the guard so I threatened him that if his behavior—the slamming of the car door, the stomping of his feet, the anger—did not improve immediately, there would be no ice cream today. Things improved immediately. Off he marched ahead of us, up the hill and around the bend in the road and out of sight. By the time the rest of us walked up the hill and around the bend in the road, there was no Philip.

No problem.

Buzz. "Philip, where are you?"

Buzz. "The cemetery."

We did not see him again until we arrived back at the SUV two hours later. We found him waiting for us. Of course, he missed the changing of the guard. But he didn't miss much else on that trip, thanks to the invention of walkie-talkies.

I had mentally replayed many times the comment made by the woman in the mothers' group about her son not appreciating the cruise, so I decided to find out what was special for my children about this trip. What had they liked the best? Number one was the elevator in the first hotel. Its parking garage was a close second. I could tell that a ride on Metro—the subway—and the SUV we rented were just slightly nudged out of the top two spots.

The day after we returned home from our trip was July 4. I was upstairs at the computer when I heard whoops and hollers coming from the TV room. I went down to find out what was so exciting. There on television was the national Fourth of July celebration on the Mall, with the Capitol in the background. Excited voices exclaimed, "We were there yesterday!" "Oh look! There's the Washington Monument!"

The elevator and the parking garage may not be the most special memories of our trip for me. But that really doesn't matter. Mine might be the night all five of us—all sharing the same room—woke up at 2:30 a.m. and stayed awake for 2 hours. There was much talking, pillow throwing, wrestling, and laughing.

Someday we may all go on a cruise together. We may not all agree about what is special, but I know already what I will be thinking. It is simple: We are going on a trip and I get to go.

Growing Up With Fragile X And Autism

Marie Horne, who served on the Board of Directors of the Autism Society of North Carolina, is the mother of two adult children, one of whom has both fragile X and autism.

My son Rob was an adorable baby who rolled over, sat up, crawled, and walked within the normal range, but by 15 months had not started talking, other than about ten words used one time only, never repeated. He never said "mommy" or "daddy," the very words we longed to hear. When he was about 18 months old, his hearing was tested and found to be normal, but the doctor spent about 5 minutes with him and said, "You have a retarded child." I was furious and felt he could not possibly know what he was talking about! However, I heeded his advice to have Rob evaluated at the Developmental Evaluation Clinic at the University of North Carolina (UNC) at Chapel Hill. After 3 days of testing, the diagnosis was "mild brain damage." The autism and fragile X diagnoses came several years later. While at the clinic, Rob and I were selected by a staff psychologist to participate in a research project to see if a mother could be taught to work with her child. I could! With the psychologist's guidance, I used a visual system to teach Rob to understand and pronounce words using the phonetic sound.

Childhood: Language Acquisition

When Rob was still young enough to ride in the seat of a grocery cart, he began to show an interest in numbers by pointing to prices affixed on shelves. Hearing about this, the psychologist told me (1) to encourage anything of interest to him, (2) to imitate any sounds he made such as little humming or bubbling noises, and (3) to use a child's dictionary to begin teaching him to recognize letters and numbers. She stressed that I should use the phonic sounds of letters.

Early Intervention Using Phonics and Visuals

I printed letters and numbers on index cards that I taped to the lower part of my refrigerator at Rob's eye level. He quickly learned to recognize and point to letters as I pronounced them using the phonic sound. *A* was "ah," *B* was "buh," *C* was "cuh," and so forth. In a few weeks he could correctly point to all the letters in the alphabet, and it was suggested that we work on three-letter words such as "dog" and "cat," so those cards joined the others on the refrigerator. Before long, Rob could recognize and point to words as I pronounced them using the phonic sounds (such as "cuh-at" for cat) and soon he began to say the words spontaneously as well as point to them. All of this happened around the time of his third birthday! Often he would omit the first letter but pronounce the correct sound, such as "oap" for "soap." Realizing that Rob needed to see words as well as hear them broken down phonetically and by syllable, I continued to build his vocabulary using the index cards until the outside of my refrigerator was covered. Thus, he learned to read before he learned to talk! It is evident that he was ready to learn but just needed to have speech broken down for him.

Along the Way

As Rob grew older, I tried to find ways to teach him new words and short sentences, never being sure that he understood the meaning and knowing he might be learning by rote. But his vocabulary expanded. He was probably learning to speak English word by word, the way some people learn to speak a second language. I tried to think of ways to demonstrate meaning. For example, I would show him an object and say "the ball is behind (under, over) the box." When Rob was about eight, in addition to my home schooling, he began years of professional speech therapy. He was fortunate to be enrolled for several years in a special classroom provided by the UNC-Chapel Hill TEACCH program (Treatment & Education of Autistic & Related Communication Handicapped Children). The highly structured environment was excellent and Rob made significant progress. He even played a role, albeit a nonspeaking one, in a Christmas play at our church.

Learning Spanish

In his teens, Rob was placed in a middle school classroom where he was the only student. Discovering that he liked the sounds of multisyllable words, his teacher decided to teach him to speak Spanish, using it as a reinforcer. Rob loved it and more than 20 years later, he can still count to 10 in Spanish. He continues to enjoy hearing what to him are interesting words with many syllables.

Sensory Integration Issues

Rob has always been sensitive to touch, bright lights, and, especially, to certain sounds. He constantly puts his hands over his ears and/or makes a humming sound to drown out other noises such as the sound of a car ignition. When he was young, he would refuse to enter a room that had balloons because he was afraid they would pop. While Rob's behaviors and adaptability have improved over time, his problems with sensory integration seem to have intensified. He now keeps the television volume turned completely off most of the time except for occasional seconds. This can be very frustrating when someone else is trying to listen to news! He also prefers to sit in a dark room with a light shining from another room. Wearing new clothing has always been a problem. New items have to be washed many times to soften them up and all labels must be removed before he will wear them.

Perfect Pitch—Musical Interests

Rob has enjoyed music therapy with piano and guitar lessons most of his life. He has perfect pitch and over the years many of his instructors envied his uncanny abilities. He can accurately identify the name of a musical note by sound alone, play guitar by ear, changing chords appropriately, and read music. Robb has a good singing voice and can play a keyboard, though at a rather primitive level.

Listening Skills

It is somewhat ironic that in spite of sensitivity to certain sounds, Rob apparently has good listening skills. In a group setting, it is easy to think he is not listening as others talk because he seldom speaks unless spoken to directly; but every now and then he will spontaneously join in a conversation carried on by people around him. Once, on a car trip when he was a teenager, his sister and father were involved in a long conversation about some sporting event, trying to remember which network was carrying a particular game. The conversation had been going on for 10 minutes or so and during a small break, Rob said (correctly) "that's ESPN." More recently, he was attending an art show where he and others with autism had work displayed. As the instructor was introducing the exhibit and artists, she paused as she momentarily forgot what she was saying. Rob spoke up with the correct word to finish her sentence! He attends a small devotional group at church but refuses to sit with others, preferring to squat just inside the doorway. If questioned afterwards, however, it is evident that he was listening because he can correctly answer questions about the presentation.

Scripts

Primarily, Rob uses what his speech therapist refers to as a script for most of his attempts at communication. He identifies cities by the number of the local television channel, so if we are going to another city, he will say, "we are going to the Three," the correct number for the local station. Or, "we are going to Market Street," a frequently visited street in a familiar town, rather than naming the town itself. He likes to have everything written down on a calendar so he will know what to expect. We always go grocery shopping when he comes home on the weekend, so this is an important date to him. He always checks it before leaving my house.

Several years ago, Rob moved into a supported living residential program with staff and two other men with autism, but he continues to come home on weekends. He is "hooked" on soft drinks, and when he is at home, he often tells me "I am out of Cokes." We fell into the habit of stopping to let him buy a Coke on his way back to his house. Recently, as he was going out the door, he was trying to tell me that we needed to buy a new supply of bottles of Coke for my house by saying, "I am out of Cokes." Mistakenly, I thought he was trying to say he wanted to stop and buy a small Coke on his way back to his house and that was his way of asking for money. I finally realized he was trying to say we would need to buy Cokes at the grocery store for him to drink on his next visit. I should have remembered that he usually says, "I am out of change," meaning he wants to stop at a drink machine. You have to pay close attention!

If you ask Rob if he wants to do something and his answer is yes, he will usually say "that's all right," or sometimes he gives a little high-pitched giggle. However, recently he has begun to answer "sure" in an appropriate context. Often I have to repeat questions to get a response, adding "Do you want to _____, YES OR NO?" Being very "tuned in" to weather reports, if he hears a severe storm or tornado warning, he will start naming the counties that are listed and you can be sure he is correct!

A form of echolalia still dominates Rob's everyday speech. He repeats things over and over, such as the exact time of day, the number of a TV channel, or comments about his dearly loved cat. Like a mother gently talking to her baby, he talks to the cat in a tender tone of voice he doesn't use otherwise, saying things such as "Who has eyes?" Over and over, he will repeat, "There's little Coo-Coo"—the name of his cat.

Rob's spontaneous speech has slowly improved over the years and now that he is an adult, it has increased significantly. Although he chatters a great deal, often he still must be prompted to respond when spoken to. But he now has an adequate amount of spontaneous speech. Simple multiple-choice questions are easier. Usually there is a small delay before he answers, because he needs time to process what has been said. He frequently refers to himself in the third person, using the pronoun "he" rather than "I"; but more and more he uses the correct pronoun. It is more difficult for him when referring to others. He will often say something about "her mother" when he really means "my mother."

Recently, Rob went in for a physical checkup with his primary care doctor, and the nurse, who has known him for a long time, asked him some questions. He promptly answered without being prodded! She expressed amazement, noting that 4 or 5 years ago he would not have answered. Usually, I tell Rob that I love him when I say goodnight and he has started to repeat, "I love you." I don't know if he really understands this or not, but I like to hear it. In the last few years he has started to snuggle up a little when I give him a hug.

One mistake I made along the way was being too quick to answer for Rob when others tried to talk with him.

E-Mail, Writing, and Checklists

Since Rob likes to use the computer, our latest adventure is using e-mail to "talk" to each other. From his day program he types in simple sentences modeled for him, such as "I miss you" or "I am going to Borders." Of course, I always respond, hoping this will continue to reinforce his understanding and his ability to use verbal language. The staff member who works with him is also using this as a means to teach rules of punctuation and capitalization. I have been told that he is becoming very independent in this effort. On weekend home visits, I also have a "written conversation" with him, writing out simple questions to which he can circle a yes or no answer.

At Creative Living, his current vocational program, Rob uses a schedule listing his daily tasks. As items are completed, he checks them off in order to earn a reinforcer at the end of the morning and afternoon. Even in adulthood we are still using as many visual cues as possible.

Rob's art therapist encourages him to write brief stories about things of interest to him, which he illustrates with simple drawings. Most of his stories involve a dog, cat, or TV. Sometimes the teacher encourages him to write about his feelings, such as being sad when a favorite uncle died. When Rob is having a good day, she says that his animals are smiling; if not, they look angry. But again, he is using visual materials to express himself and his feelings. Whether or not people with autism have feelings has been questioned by some, but I am sure Rob does. He is very empathetic when people around him are in stress. In one of his vocational programs there were several people in wheelchairs, and he would frequently go over and gently touch them on the head. This from a person who "ignores" others! He adores cats, both his own and those belonging to other people. However, he has been known to kiss inanimate objects.

Adolescence and Adulthood: Problems At School And Work

During Rob's teen years his aggressive behaviors became more prevalent. This was due at least in part to his school placement, which was entirely inappropriate—and later, by futile attempts to "fit" into vocational programs designed for persons with mental retardation.

"I quit," said Rob, stamping his feet and repeating it again and again. After several years of trying without success to work in a bakery designed primarily for people with mental retardation, he had had it. The staff had tried to help him adjust, but being a loner, he just could not tolerate a program in which everyone worked as a member of a team and where there were no clear-cut work processes or schedules for which he was responsible. Rob had tried, but the program was not right for him. He said he wanted to be a bakery supervisor! There was little structure, and the staff members were not trained to work with people with autism. But because there was no other vocational program in the area designed for people with autism, I refused to let him quit until one day he had a severe temper tantrum, threw furniture and other objects across the room, and hit several of his co-workers. Actually, less severe episodes like this had occurred once or twice before, but this time he was suspended from the program and not allowed to return.

Rob had dropped out of school at 17 because he could not cope with the class to which he was assigned. The public school system failed to provide a class that could meet his needs, resulting in extreme frustration and escalating behavior problems. He had been allowed to attend high school for 2 years even though a suitable class was not available; but, because of behavior problems and lack of progress, he was reassigned to a class located in a K-3 school! He was humiliated! I met with the local school board and eventually his class was moved to a middle school, but he had been used to attending high school and knew he was not supposed to be with younger children. After several frustrating months, Rob refused to go to school and I had no choice but to let him drop out. At that point, I began to explore opportunities for vocational training in the rural town where we lived, quickly finding there were few options available.

First, he tried to work at a local sheltered workshop, in a program designed for people who were able to function productively with no behavior problems and minimal supervision. Rob was the only person there with fragile X and autism. The workshop had agreed to give him a 6-week trial period, but at the end of the trial he was dismissed as being "not ready." From there he went into an ADAP (Adult Developmental Activity Program) that served primarily lower functioning persons with mental retardation. Again, Rob was very frustrated and humiliated. His unacceptable behaviors multiplied. He began to kick holes in the walls and door of his room. We replaced his bedroom door three times until I finally gave up and just covered over the holes with a piece of poster paper. About that time I realized that because of his strength, I could no longer control him physically and psychology wasn't working either! Several months later, an opportunity for placement in an ICF-MR (Intermediate Care Facility for the Mentally Retarded) group home for adults with autism became available and he was accepted for admission. I did this reluctantly, but knew I could no longer manage him at home. The placement was fairly satisfactory but he still had no appropriate employment opportunities.

The next step was a move to our state capital—Raleigh, North Carolina—where I hoped to find a suitable program for him. At this point Rob had moved back home with me. We visited two vocational programs. One was a sheltered workshop, which Rob hated from the moment he walked in. He kept trying to pull me out as I discussed the program with the staff. The other was the bakery I've mentioned. This program was good for those for whom it was designed, but not for Rob. So, for the next 6 months after being suspended, he had nothing to do. After we moved to Raleigh, he had moved into a second ICF-MR group home and it was a struggle for the staff to try to keep him occupied. My son had to endure more than 8 years of one frustrating experience after another. He was not a happy camper and needless to say, neither was I. But I was determined to do something about it.

Creative Living: Vocational Program For Adults With Autism

Talking with other parents, it became evident to me that there was a need for a different type of vocational program for adults with autism and/or fragile X. Two other mothers and I formed a committee and collected signatures on a petition asking the board of directors of the Autism Society of North Carolina (ASNC) to appoint a Task Force for Vocational Alternatives to include parents and professionals. I was appointed as a co-chair of the Task Force. The goal was to design a vocational program we felt would meet the unique needs and abilities of our sons and daughters, building on their individual strengths, adjusting for their weaknesses, and promoting activities that would enrich their lives. We visited existing vocational programs across North Carolina, including the Enrichment Center in Winston-Salem.

The Enrichment Center is a vocational program featuring activities such as cooking, dancing, and crafts. It serves people with varying disabilities, including autism. We also visited CSAAC (Community Services for Autistic Adults & Children) in Baltimore. The Maryland program consisted primarily of supported employment activities combined with supported living arrangements in apartments or houses.

This was a big step for many people who had previously lived in large institutions. Both programs inspired us. We were also inspired by a video of a successful program for people with autism in Israel that utilizes art and music as an integral part of its program. This "struck a chord" with us and we adopted those components, along with others. The Task Force included professionals from the UNC-Chapel Hill TEACCH program who served as consultants and helped us to plan the program we had in mind.

As the Task Force met over a period of months, we tried to determine what the ideal program would be for a person with fragile X and autism. We wanted it to be stimulating, with staff trained in the TEACCH methods who understood the special characteristics, needs, and strengths of persons with fragile X and autism. We did not want our sons and daughters to be "warehoused" in an isolated setting, performing boring, repetitive work. We wanted the program to be one that we, as parents, would enjoy!

The program was approved by ASNC, and we were successful in getting a sizeable grant from the North Carolina General Assembly. A suitable building was found, staff were hired and trained in the TEACCH methods (structured teaching) and the doors were opened. The name "Creative Living" was chosen, and the first five participants were enrolled, one of whom was my son, Rob.

The basic components of the Creative Learning Program include art, music, recreation therapies, supported employment and/or volunteer work, lifelong learning, community outings, and studio crafts. Creative Living serves 15 participants (we refuse to call them "clients"), some of whom attend part time. The program is managed by ASNC, but a strong partnership with parents is encouraged. Staff consists of a program director, program assistant, art therapist, music therapist, vocational specialist, recreation specialist, studio crafts specialists, and general instructors. Each participant has an individualized schedule, tailored to match his/her personal interests, strengths, and areas of need. A simple checklist using numerous visual systems enables participants to transition easily from one activity to another throughout the day.

Some use a picture schedule; others are able to read and follow a written schedule. Checks are earned and then rewarded twice a day. Several participants have a dual diagnosis. In addition to autism, one person also has cerebral palsy, two have fragile X, and one is deaf. Sign language is used for those who need it.

The participants are thriving in this environment. The specialists work with participants individually and in special group activities, such as music & movement and social skills. Meaningful yet pleasurable recreational activities include visits to museums, sports arenas, public services, concerts, or whatever is available. Several participants, including Rob, go to a wellness center at a local hospital for exercise, thus participating in "real life" activities. The recreation therapist tries to find games or activities enjoyed by each individual. For example, my son enjoys watching *Wheel of Fortune*, so a similar board game was purchased for him. It's used not only for enjoyment but also to reinforce his understanding of money. We feel recreation is an area that meets a great need because many people with autism have limited leisure skills. There is a saying that speaks volumes: "Work is leisure and leisure is work for people with autism."

Several of the participants excel in art, and the group hosts one or two art shows in the community each year, including shows at the Raleigh Little Theatre. In addition to encouraging traditional artwork, the therapist helps participants express themselves, especially in coping with negative feelings and anxieties. For example, two men in the program have lost a parent. The therapist worked with them to prepare booklets that would help them cope with grief. Rob, who has limited expressive language, enjoys making little booklets that include a story about his pet cat—his favorite subject. Included in the booklets are his illustrations. The therapist says she can tell when Rob is concerned about something. If he is happy, the cat is smiling. If not, the cat's teeth are bared in anger!

Several years ago, Creative Living acquired a kiln and started a studio crafts component. The center purchases raw pottery—vases, soap dishes, and bowls, for example—which the participants paint. The objects are then fired in the kiln and sold at conferences or wherever an opportunity arises. Participants are paid a portion of the profits based on sales of products they make. Rob loves this and makes up interesting little sounds to accompany each of his brush strokes. Another source of income is from in-house janitorial services, such as cleaning and vacuuming, for which participants are paid minimum wage.

Volunteer work in the community is popular with the participants. One morning a week they work at the Food Bank of North Carolina, assembling packets of food and performing other jobs as needed. Several participants work in Meals on Wheels, delivering food to invalids (driven by staff, of course). One group sets tables once a week for a senior citizens club in a local church. Another group visits the Society for the Prevention of Cruelty to Animals where they do chores such as washing windows. As an added benefit, they get to pet and play with the animals. These activities help to fulfill our goal to make it possible for our family members to participate in the community as much as possible, while also receiving vocational training.

This program has been a lifeline for Rob. He is happy, looks forward to attending Creative Living, and leaves reluctantly at the end of the day. He goes around to tell each staff member good-bye in his own way. His behaviors have improved dramatically, and he has not had a temper tantrum in several years. Expressive language is increasing because the staff understands how to draw him out and interact with him, tolerate his silly chatter, and generally meet him at his level. He no longer feels like a misfit; this is a group where he "belongs." Each day at Creative Living is different but every Monday is just like all other Mondays, and so on. Since he lives in a residential program, also run by the Autism Society of North Carolina, the staff there interacts with him in the same manner. So from early morning until bedtime, he has a calm yet stimulating, predictable, structured environment. That relieves Rob's anxiety because he knows exactly what to expect. In his residential program he has learned to do his own laundry, help prepare meals, and do simple household chores. When he comes home on weekends, I find that he likes to do small chores at home, too. I am thankful that he finally has the opportunity to live and work in a setting where he can grow, develop, do things he enjoys, and just be himself. No one is trying to make him into some model he can never achieve.

All Grown Up

When Rob was first diagnosed, I was told that if he did not start talking by age 5, he would likely be mute the rest of his life. So I am very thankful for the progress he has made. Even though he primarily uses his "script" for verbal communication, and it tends to be stilted and repetitive, I am pleased that he can express his wishes and concerns to let me know if he feels bad or wants something. The good news is that in the last 6 or 7 years he has apparently gained the ability to comprehend and use words correctly without their having been specifically taught to him, as I did in his early years. He often surprises me with a word that I had no idea he knew. The ability to talk is also enhanced by his excellent reading ability. He reads newspapers, especially the television channel guide and the sports section, and, of all things, the obituaries! He still likes numbers and dates. It is evident that Rob was ready to recognize numbers, letters, and words even at a young age. Otherwise the use of phonics and visual cues would not have been effective in stimulating spoken language. In his case, it was well worth the time and effort spent working with him. Stilted language and "talking in script" are better than being mute!

As Rob grew up, our family also grew up. Living with a person who has fragile X and autism has an impact on the family, especially siblings. It was hard for Rob's younger sister to understand him when they were young and why, in her eyes, he received "better" treatment than she did. As an adult, she still has some unhappy memories. In families with a person with a disability, stress is inevitable, and it affects everyone.

Rob is now almost 42 years old and seems happy. He has a good sense of humor and frequently gives funny nicknames to people he knows. Almost every person who has worked with him over the years has told me they enjoyed it because he was fun to work with. I always found it rewarding because he is very receptive to learning if information is presented in the right way. Acquiring verbal language skills, however, has been a lifelong process and is still a work in progress.

Creative Living has given my son a place like the old television show *Cheers*, where everyone knows his name! He loves it, he's very contented, and no longer is he an unhappy camper. Neither am I. Finally, Rob has found his place in the world.

Dear Andrew

Rosanna Walther, whose grandson was recently diagnosed with fragile X, is an elementary school secretary and freelance writer.

"Fragile X?" our voices say in unison. You can hear the question in our tone. We've never heard of fragile X before, nor did we know it was a genetic anomaly. Although we wondered if the delays you experienced in sitting up and rolling over were due to the jaundice you were hospitalized with shortly after birth, and why you didn't try to imitate funny faces as most babies do, you were a lovable baby. You loved to be cuddled, eat, laugh, and watch Baby Picasso. In short, you captured our hearts.

Dear Andrew,

"Before I formed you in the womb, I knew you" (Jeremiah 1:5 NKJ).

Just so, from the moment we heard you were going to be born, Grandma and Poppy loved you. Even before we knew you would be Andrew Gallo Miller, you held a special place in our hearts. Poppy ordered a miniature New England dory, the wooden rocking boat you and your sister love to play in when you visit us.

The first time your mom and dad left you to spend the weekend at our house by yourself you were 9 months old. You didn't crawl or walk yet and you weighed 26 lbs. Every time I carried you upstairs to change your diaper or put you to sleep, I had to stop in the middle of the staircase to catch my breath and tighten my grip on you. My heart would be pounding when we finally reached the top of the stairs.

That was the first time I saw my weight as a health issue and not just a fashion problem. It affected and limited what I could do with you and threatened the time I might have to spend with you. That was all the motivation I needed to begin a diet. Weight Watchers helped change my eating habits and start exercising. I lost 45 pounds.

Now I can run with you. And energy we need, for you are full of energy and life. Often you rise before dawn to greet the morning and race through the day. A blur of color, you whirl and enchant us with your ocean blue eyes and big dimpled smile. As most little boys, you are fascinated with cars, trucks, and machinery. Whenever we pass a construction site, we pull to the side of the road so you can give us a narrative on what the payloader is doing (moving dirt), while asking questions at the same time, like "What are they building?" and "When will they finish?"

You love to come to our house on Long Island to visit and go for boat rides with Poppy on the *Maddie G*. The added bonus is visiting with your Uncle Dan who owns a property management business. You get to see how his equipment operates up close and sometimes he takes you with him to deliver materials and plants to job sites. You especially loved the time you rode with him in the cab of his dump truck to drop debris at the town landfill.

Feelings are intangible, yet we express those emotions outwardly. As you have learned to put names to the tangible items that inhabit our world, we pray you are able to put names to the emotions you feel— love, happiness, excitement, anger, frustration, remorse, forgiveness— and learn appropriate ways to deal with them. As a toddler we could tell how excited you were when we came to visit. We could see you dancing up and down on your toes through the front door, but before we could enter you would be hiding in another room.

Everyone looks at things differently and likes different things. I'm afraid of heights and won't go on a roller coaster, while your mom and dad love roller coaster rides. You don't like the noise and confusion of a three-ring circus, but you love to bowl and knock down pins.

Fragile X is something you have, but it cannot and does not define you or who you will become. You are extra special, yet you are the same as everyone else. We are all fragile and special, wanting and needing love and acceptance from our family, the companionship of friends, and the fulfillment of a job well done.

Andrew, know that you are loved beyond measure, without limit and infinitely, first by God and your parents and then those of us privileged to be part of your life.

I don't know what your dreams or aspirations will be when you grow up. You are still in the process of discovery. You might want to run a business like your Uncle Dan so you can drive the trucks you love to watch now, or be a quarterback because you love to watch football and root for the Seahawks with your dad. I just don't want any labels or preconceived ideas to keep you from setting goals and striving to achieve them.

How far can you go? As far as the eye can see and you desire, because "with God all things are possible" (Matthew 19:26 NIV). Live with love and kindness, and go further and further to achieve and fulfill all God has purposed and intended for your life.

We'll always be in the stands rooting and praying for you.

Love always,
Grandma

An Extended Family Perspective: Interview With Kathryn And Allison Ridlon

Charles W. Luckmann is the co-editor of **X Stories**. *He has two children, Arielle (21), who is not a carrier; and Noah (15), who has the full fragile X mutation.*

On a day in December 2005, with snow covering the ground, I met with Kathryn and Allison Ridlon at their home in a rural section of Pierce County, southeast of Tacoma, Washington. Kathryn prefers to be called Kitty, and Allison goes by the nickname Angel. We had met a year and a half earlier on Capitol Hill in Washington, DC, during the first ever Advocacy Day for fragile X syndrome. During Advocacy Day we were lobbying Congress to support additional funding—channeled through the National Institutes of Health and the Centers for Disease Control—for research and educational outreach related to improving family life for those with fragile X syndrome.

Both Kitty and Angel fit the mold of other devoted and articulate fragile X moms I've met. But Kitty is feisty and strong-willed and does most of the talking. Maybe it's because she's a great-grandmother and seen a lot. "Those who get heard are often the most persistent," she says.

When I first met her on that hot and humid June day in Washington, she and Angel were slowly making the rounds of Capitol Hill. Slowly because Kitty had to stop every 100 feet or so to rest, but that didn't dampen the fire in her belly. During the frequent stops she talked passionately, as she did again to me on this day in December, about how she desperately wants a cure for fragile X. She wants doctors and the public to be better educated. She wants better resources, especially in the schools—but also in every community throughout North America and the world. "It shouldn't make a difference where you live," she said, "or how much money you make, in order to get the resources you need to live a decent life."

Angel was dressed fashionably, as was her mother. When I first met Angel in June 2004, she appeared a youthful mother in her late 30s or early 40s. What was most striking was her long, flowing blond hair, reminding you—yes—of an angel. But today a black hat, sporting a diamond-like brooch, covered her head. After months of chemotherapy Angel no longer had feet upon feet of flowing hair. But nothing diminished her smile when I asked how she was doing. "Really good," she said, and then she explained that the cancer in her body was in remission. "The doctors think my recovery may be attributable to genetics," she said. "The fragile X gene, which caused my POF (premature ovarian failure), may have helped my body fight the cancer, at least that's what my doctor said. He said malignant tumors in women feed off of estrogen. Because of POF my estrogen level was low, which helped reduce my tumor."

A few weeks after my afternoon with Kitty and Angel I checked the National Fragile X Foundation Web site to learn more about menopause and POF. Menopause typically happens in women between the ages of 45-55. POF can precipitate an early onset of menopause, before age 45, or it can precipitate what health-care providers are now calling "ovarian insufficiency," a form of infertility that may ebb and flow before the onset of menopause. I learned that 21 percent of women who carry the fragile X gene experience some form of ovarian insufficiency and 23 percent experience early menopause.

Angel has two children. Randy is 15 years old and Steven is 12. Randy is unaffected, but Steven expresses a full mutation of the fragile X gene. He inherited fragile X from Angel, who carries the premutation that she inherited from Kitty. Kitty inherited the premutation from her mother or father, who presumably inherited it from their parents. Kitty said she and Angel wanted to talk about their family history as a way to shine a flashlight on the fragile X disease, to allow others to see its effects more clearly. They want the public to be better informed. They think this will help everyone.

During our afternoon conversation, seated around an oval oak table drinking Cokes and eating sandwiches, Angel explained some of the interpersonal dynamics between her two sons. "Randy is embarrassed by Steven," she said. "When we're out in public as a family unit, Randy tends to separate himself from us, walking either ahead or behind us." She laughs. "When we were visiting Disneyland recently he pretended he wasn't with us. At home he doesn't act that way. But I guess in public he's embarrassed by Steven's behavior."

Steven is in the fifth grade with age-appropriate peers. Angel has advocated strongly that Steven stay with his peer group even though, according to her, the school district has wanted to place Steven with the more severely disabled and mentally retarded in the school's Life Skills program. "Steven mimics what other kids do," said Angel. "I want him mimicking what a typical fifth grader does. He learns from other kids; in a lot of ways he's a typical kid."

Steven is high functioning, a good example of how broad the fragile X spectrum can be. He is toilet trained and rides a bike—skills some fragile X boys his age, like my son, Noah, are incapable of doing. Though Steven is for the most part mainstreamed with his fifth-grade class, "he struggles with academic subjects," said Angel. "He's removed from the classroom each day for reading and math with a "Resource Room" teacher, a special education instructor."

Kitty and Angel dream of Steven becoming a contributing member of society, but it's difficult sometimes just to get him to the activity. "We once tried to take Steven to a Fourth of July parade, but he screamed all the way there," related Angel. "I know a lot of people were thinking, 'don't force him to watch if he doesn't want to,' but once we got him there and his anxiety lessened, he started to enjoy it. And then he became very obsessive-compulsive about parades," said Angel laughing. "But I want Steven to do what other kids his age do."

Steven is different, but not obviously disabled. Some people with the full fragile X mutation are severely mentally retarded, but others like Steven are high functioning, and still others are somewhere in between. There's tremendous diversity within the fragile X phenotype and its visible parameters. Because the phenotype of fragile X that Steven exhibits is different enough to draw attention from his peers, but not different enough to get their sympathy or compassion, Kitty and Angel worry about how Steven will be treated next year in middle school, and then later in high school. They worry about whether or not Steven will be accepted into his school community. They worry about him later in life. Will he integrate successfully into their small hometown, and the rural community of Pierce County? This is part of what motivates Angel to struggle with Steven's elementary school to keep him with his age group. She wants the school to give him the help he needs without separating him from his fifth-grade peers.

Kitty's worry for her grandson Steven comes naturally. She has a 45-year-old son with the full fragile X mutation. His name is Gordon. He was born in 1960. But it wasn't until physicians diagnosed her grandson Steven with fragile X in 1997 that Kitty had Gordon tested for fragile X and realized that her family was passing the FMR1 gene from generation to generation. Kitty insisted that no doctor or healthcare provider ever hinted at the possibility that because her son Gordon is cognitively disabled, her other children and grandchildren were at risk.

When Steven was very young Angel began to notice hand flapping and other developmental characteristics associated with her brother Gordon. Angel went to her pediatrician and said, "We really need to find out what's going on." But Angel related to me that her pediatrician asked, "Do you really want to open up a can of worms?"

Angel switched to a different pediatrician, who had Steven tested for fragile X. "As soon as Steven tested positive I knew Gordon had fragile X too," said Angel.

Kitty told another story illustrating how doctors aren't well enough informed about fragile X; she related about a family who had three children with fragile X before they were diagnosed. "It's critically important," she said, "that pediatricians get up to speed on diagnosing fragile X."

"They test every mother-to-be over 30 for Down syndrome," said Angel, "why not for fragile X? Why not test every baby after it's born?"

"Insurance companies wouldn't pay for it," countered Kitty.

"But screening every mother-to-be and infant would be fantastic. I'm against abortion," continued Kitty, "but every mother should make that decision for herself....I don't know," she mused, enunciating each syllable clearly, "but I may have found a way to terminate the pregnancy had I known at the time."

But now she knows that what she went through with Gordon was not her fault. As we sat around the table talking, Kitty explained that during the 1960s when her son was growing up and it was becoming clear that he was cognitively challenged, she frequently blamed herself. Even though she was a careful mother-to-be when pregnant, until she got the fragile X diagnosis she blamed herself for more than three decades. "I felt guilty," she said. "'What did I do wrong during pregnancy?' was a question I frequently asked myself."

As Kitty talked, her grief for the decades of guilt and self-blaming, and relief in the knowledge that is now possible, were palpable. During

183

the interview Kitty and Angel emphasized emphatically, and again and again, how important a correct diagnosis is for getting on with life. "When Gordon was 2 years old he was diagnosed with cerebral palsy," Kitty said. "That was the catchall in the 1960s, but that diagnosis never really fit for Gordon."

Kitty's story and family tree are typical of other families with fragile X, passing from generation to generation an unstable FMR1 gene. At a recent one-day meeting about fragile X on the University of Washington's Medical School campus, Dr. Paul Hagerman, a leading researcher on the genetics of fragile X, told those gathered that fragile X syndrome has been part of the human gene pool "for a very long time....We now know that fragile X is even found in other primate populations," he said.

Back in the 1930s Kitty's mother, Frances, or maybe her father, passed the fragile X gene to Kitty. Kitty's biological father died when she was young, so Kitty doesn't know 100 percent if she inherited fragile X from her father or mother. But she suspects her mother, because, as Kitty related, Frances was "tight-lipped" about family genealogy.

Kitty found out later in life that she had an older sibling she didn't know she had—"either given up for adoption or institutionalized." And when Kitty asked Frances for information, Frances was defensive about the family history.

Kitty suspects that Frances carried the premutation because once it was obvious that Gordon was mentally challenged, she stopped showing any interest in him. Moreover, once her great-grandchild was diagnosed with fragile X, Frances lost interest in Steven, too. Kitty thinks that her mother was ashamed of, and felt guilty for, mental disabilities in the family. This was a common attitude in those days.

"During my marriage to my first husband, my in-laws wouldn't give Gordon presents; they would only give presents to my oldest son, who was typical," said Kitty, as she continued talking about the past. "They didn't want to acknowledge that there was a disabled child in the family. But I wouldn't let them discriminate. They had to give presents to both." She paused, and then said, "Fragile X makes you a better person, but it can tear families apart."

"Back in the 60s and 70s when Gordon was growing up there was a stigma attached to having a disabled child. Today people don't look at Steven like they used to look at Gordon. I got a lot of hostile looks back in the 60s when I'd take Gordon out in public. Back then they wanted the disabled out of sight. Once when Gordon was out shopping with me a woman came up and said, 'If I had a child like that I'd keep him at home.'"

"I don't want others to go through what I did," Kitty said. "The hours I lay awake at night crying myself to sleep wanting a better life for Gordon. I wouldn't wish that experience on anyone. But fragile X showed me I'm more capable than I ever imagined. It's made me a better person, but I wish things had been different for Gordon. I would want to change it for Gordon.

"Things are better now for Allison than they were for me. But you don't want your child to experience pain like you did. That's where public awareness comes in. I raised Gordon when there wasn't much public acceptance of difference.

"Yet when friends or acquaintances, or teachers or potential caregivers ask about Gordon, and I say he has fragile X syndrome, most people still ask, 'What is that?'

"I want people to know about fragile X."

"I'm more into research than public awareness," countered Angel. "I want people to know if they're a carrier. I want all mothers and babies tested. Eventually I want a cure."

"But without the public awareness you don't get the money for research," said Kitty.

"Without the research there's no hope. The research has to come first. Without the research there's no reason to get it out to the public."

"I can't break it down into what's most important. What's more important, the chicken or the egg?" laughed Kitty. "When you stop and realize how many people carry the fragile X gene, it's amazing more people don't know about it."

Dear Jess: A Letter To My Son

*Judy Stringer is a carrier of fragile X and mother to a child
with the full mutation.*

Dear Jess, I love you and think about you every day.

Your early years were not easy. We didn't get your fragile X
diagnosis until you were 9 years old. Up until that time and all through
your school years, Dad and I fought with the school district for every
special service you needed and we even took you to private speech and
occupational therapy classes in a town an hour's drive from home. You
had all the tests and scans and developed a fear and mistrust of doctors.

We did our best to expose you to things the other kids did. We just
had to alter and adjust our view. You and your sister, Jea, loved the trip
to Disneyland we took in the midst of a drizzle. No crowds or lines at
any of the rides. You were unable to wait in lines and this was a perfect
solution.

It took time, but we helped you master a two-wheel bicycle and you
enjoyed riding your mountain bike all over town.

Living in Tahoe, Dad, Jea, your big brother Jimmy, and I all skied
and we tried and tried to teach you. Finally I took you to a ski school
for the handicapped at Alpine Meadows and it finally clicked. Of

course, we only skied on sunny days and always relaxed with a long lunch. With you, the process was to be enjoyed. When you skied on the Special Olympics team, we were so proud of you. You didn't care if you won, you just were thrilled to see us all cheering you on.

Jess, you made everything fun with your easy smile and contagious laughter. You truly enjoyed every person you came in contact with.

We knew you would never get a driver's license, but you wanted to drive so badly. Dad would take you and Jea out on the back roads and hills and teach you how to drive our old truck. You got very good and even could back up with considerable skill.

We had a philosophy that you could learn anything you wanted to. It would just take a little longer and we would have to be creative and make it fun.

Why would anyone want to learn something if it's not enjoyable? You loved music so much, and after a few tries we hit on someone who had the skill, patience, and fun personality to teach you guitar. Again we learned not to focus on a result, but to focus on the joy of learning— to play chords, pick strings, and strum. You didn't care if you played a song, but you reveled in the music.

I knew how important it was for you to look as much like the other kids as possible. You couldn't button your Levi 501 jeans so I took them to be altered and the seamstress took out the buttons and put in a snap above the zipper. Whenever you got new jeans or khakis they went first to the seamstress to get snaps put on. As you grew into adulthood you learned to button.

Tying shoes was another story. You never mastered tying a knot or bow. But so what? There were slip-on Vans and many other cool shoes without laces. Loafers were another favorite. You had a hard time combing your hair so it was kept short.

There's always a way. I know. Being a parent of a fragile X child makes us creative!

When you were 19 we went to Mexico for 5 weeks. We had some Honda scooters to drive around and you surprised me at how fast you mastered those. You would drive into town by yourself with a pocketful of pesos and buy a soda or music tape.

When we returned home we bought you a scooter, and you rode it constantly on the back roads and at the 5-acre yard where our business was located.

You loved to watch the cooking shows on television. When you helped me in the kitchen, you were excited to show me what you had learned. You became knowledgeable about food, and even your sister was surprised at your cooking accomplishments.

School was difficult and you hated going. Finally, in high school, we had enough. We pulled you out and did our own home schooling and got you involved with chores and similar helpful activities. You enjoyed going to the "young adults group," where you excelled socially and were able to relax with those who accepted you as you were.

Your family and friends were important to you, too. You adored your big brother, Jimmy, and sister, Jea. You loved to go out to breakfast with Gramma, to concerts in the park with Aunt Sue, and excursions into the city—or anywhere else to explore—with your Uncle John. You enjoyed seeing and being with everyone.

Jess, you became such a loving, accepting, and happy young adult. We made sure we treated you with unlimited amounts of love, acceptance, respect, and happiness.

I love you and think about you every day. And I miss you terribly.

Mom

(Jess went to heaven on March 5, 2002. His heart failed suddenly, because of mitral valve prolapse. He was 25 years old.)

Artist: Amy DeBernardis

Amy DeBernardis was diagnosed with fragile X when she was 12 years old. She currently works at Family Outreach in Bozeman, Montana.

Professionals & Caregivers

Carriers

*Marcia L. Braden is a psychologist who has presented at
numerous conferences about fragile X syndrome and autism.*

They're called carriers
because they carry a specific gene
they pass on to their children.

I call them carriers
because they carry all the hopes
and dreams possible for their children.
They carry their fears, anxiety, struggles,
defeat and pain. They are capable of carrying
the joy of success and the disappointment
of developmental delays all at the same time.
They carry a favorite toy, an old picture or
funny cap that brings comfort and security
wherever they go. They carry mental ammunition
to their school placement; staffings
and strategies for treatment. They carry
the strength to defy all odds and march on
with fortified courage and unconditional love.

These are the carriers I know.

Fragile X: A Family Affair

Louise W. Gane is currently a researcher at the M.I.N.D. Institute and has been involved in fragile X research for more than 20 years.

Let me tell you a story. A story about a family. A family that, like many families with whom I have worked, taught me much of what I know about the human side of fragile X. None of us realized when we first met that we would be learning and growing together over many years.

It was 1991. I was scheduled to see a family from Alaska who had come to see Dr. Randi Hagerman and our team for an evaluation at the Fragile X Treatment and Research Center in Denver. The parents had brought in their son and daughter who had been diagnosed with fragile X, as had their older half brother who was not with them. Another brother who did not have fragile X accompanied them.

During the evaluation, the parents shared themselves and their story with us. The mother's first marriage resulted in a child who had been diagnosed with mental impairment/developmental delay. After his birth, his mother was divorced and met her present husband. Their first child, a son, was born and developed as expected. There were

194

no concerns. A second child—another son—and their third child, a daughter, followed. As the last two children grew, delays were seen. Eventually they and their half brother were diagnosed with fragile X syndrome.

What could we do to help them? What did we have to suggest that would help their children? These questions and many others were asked. Some we could answer. Others we could not. I talked with the family in order to identify other family members at risk. Since the mother was an only child and her mother had remarried and had six other children and many grandchildren who had no problems, it was felt that the maternal grandfather must be the carrier of the FMR1 gene mutation. However, blood was drawn from the mother and the three visiting children to ascertain their FMR1 gene status. It was requested that the maternal grandmother be tested. Arrangements were made by telephone. Eventually a blood sample was taken and analyzed by our molecular laboratory.

At 2 p.m. on a Wednesday, three weeks after the blood had been received, the maternal grandmother in this story called me. She asked for her blood test result. It was positive! The grandmother carried the FMR1 gene mutation. This was an unexpected result and illustrates the necessity of having testing performed to determine FMR1 gene status.

After I gave her the result, the grandmother asked questions regarding risks to her children and grandchildren and/or to having a child with fragile X. I explained that each of her six children from her second marriage were at risk to carry the gene mutation. In addition, I was able to explain the risks for her grandchildren. As we talked, she identified her relatives who still lived in Ireland. She, her children, and grandchildren were the only family living in America. After some time, she decided that her questions had been answered and said good-bye.

I hung up the phone and felt uneasy. Something was wrong but I didn't know what it was. I worried that perhaps she was not handling the information well. Perhaps she needed something that I had not been able to provide. Perhaps she needed support in dealing with the information. Perhaps she wasn't coping appropriately. I just felt something was wrong.

The following Wednesday at 2 p.m., I called her and spoke to her husband, who called her to the phone. I asked how she was doing. How was she handling the information? Had she shared with anyone what she had learned? What was she feeling? It became clear that she was grieving and was having trouble integrating into her self-image the information that she had received. We talked for an hour. We talked about the genetic information as well as things that we had in common—children, grandchildren, being born and raised in another country. Still, I worried about her and how she was coping. I offered to call her the following week at 2 p.m. So, we made a deal. I would call her every Wednesday at 2 p.m., but if I didn't remember or if I couldn't call, she would call me. She would not be alone.

Over the course of 6 months, the weekly calls were made. Although I encouraged her to contact a professional counselor to help her cope emotionally with the genetic information and its implications, she would not do so. We continued to share and I learned about her family, who was everything to her. With time, she remembered a nephew in Ireland who was considered to be "different." He was never allowed to leave the house, was never seen by anyone—not family, friends, or neighbors. She realized that he probably had fragile X. She began to share the information I gave her with her sons and daughters from her second marriage. They began to call with questions and then to make testing arrangements through me. I encouraged them to contact a counselor in their area, but they wanted to work with me as I had worked with their mother and sister. Family members were tested: an engineer, a test pilot, an entrepreneur, a mother, and others. I talked with each about risks for their children and future offspring as well as the choices and options available to them. We talked about coping with the genetic information and the emotional ramifications of grief, guilt, denial, and eventual movement toward acceptance. Time passed.

Eventually, the calls began to space out and occurred with less frequency. However, we never completely lost touch. The National

Fragile X Foundation Conference was scheduled to be held at Snowmass, Colorado, and we arranged to meet. It was with great excitement that we met and exchanged a big warm hug! A bond had been formed through a shared experience. It was a bond that would not be broken.

Later, a daughter called because she was pregnant. I helped her work with her physicians so that she was able to have prenatal testing. The baby was a boy who did not carry the FMR1 gene mutation.

A granddaughter called. She was a high school student body president. Because we had tested her when she was younger, she knew that she was a carrier of the gene mutation. As student body president she had never had trouble talking at the assemblies, but recently she had started to have panic attacks that were interfering with her ability to speak publicly. Were panic attacks associated with the FMR1 gene mutation? I explained that they were. It was suggested that she may wish to try medication. She called me back to say that the medication had worked well and that she was going on to college. Several years later, she called to tell me that she had graduated from college, was married, and pregnant. I helped her to arrange prenatal testing and she had a little boy who did not carry the gene mutation.

At the National Fragile X Foundation meeting held in Portland, Oregon, one of the sons introduced himself to me. He told me that the family thought that his mother was extremely depressed after learning that she carried the FMR1 premutation. They were afraid that she might be suicidal. They had tried to get her to go to counseling, but she wouldn't do so. Being brought up in Ireland, counseling was not acceptable to her. However, she could talk with me every week. From him, I learned how important it is to follow through with families and to take the time to be there when needed. I learned that a clinician can make a difference even though at the time they are not aware of the impact they may have. He felt that the phone calls between his mother and me had made all the difference in helping her to cope and move on with her life. I hope so.

Time passed. I continued to be in touch with the family as needed or when an important family event occurred. I received a high school prom photo. I received a graduation announcement. I watched the brother without fragile X make friends at the National Fragile X Foundation Conference in Los Angeles. When I saw him again, he was a United States Marine. The original family moved from Alaska to Wyoming. Marriages and births occurred. Time passed.

The Fragile X Center relocated from Denver to the University of California's M.I.N.D. Institute at Davis and continued under the leadership of Dr. Hagerman. I made the move too. It was during this time that we identified fragile X-associated tremor ataxia syndrome (FXTAS). Members of the fragile X team under Dr. Hagerman's leadership began a FXTAS Californian prevalence study. We traveled throughout California visiting families in their homes as we carried out the research protocol. With time, a visit to the grandmother was arranged as part of this protocol.

It was with real pleasure that we met again. Although there had been health problems and she had had a series of strokes, the grandmother was in good spirits. She and her husband participated in the study. During the visit, it became evident that she had FXTAS. In fact, she was one of the first Californian women identified with FXTAS. We talked to them both about the implications of our finding. They hoped to come to northern California to participate in more detailed studies with us in the near future. However, this became impossible to arrange as her health deteriorated.

Not long ago, I received a call from a daughter in Oregon. She was involved in transporting her parents so that she could watch over them. We talked in detail about FXTAS and the other health issues of her mother. The trip was made successfully. Her parents were relocated. Since this daughter was the legal guardian of her parents, we were able to arrange for a tissue donation from the grandmother upon her death. Through this gift, the grandmother will be able to give to others. The information gained through research will allow us to move forward in understanding and treating FXTAS and fragile X. Her generosity is typical of her spirit and her dedication to her children and grandchildren with and without fragile X.

The story of this family does not have an ending. The family is large and it continues to grow and expand. They, like other families, have given me the privilege of sharing their lives. They have taught me the meaning of truly listening and providing support to all family members. Through them, I have learned much about living with fragile X and the gene change that causes not only fragile X but also FXTAS. Through them, I have grown as a professional and as a person. To them and all the families who have a child with fragile X, I can only say simply but with real warmth and true appreciation: thank you!

Genetic Researcher: Interview With Dr. Charles Laird

Charles W. Luckmann is the co-editor of **X Stories**. *He has two children, Arielle (21), who is not a carrier; and Noah (15), who has the full fragile X mutation.*

Charles Laird arrived at his office in Kincaid Hall on the University of Washington campus carrying a bicycle helmet and a backpack, smiling but looking pale. He apologized for being late; he was coming from a physical therapy appointment to help relieve a lower back injury. Regardless of the back injury, he had bicycled to his therapy appointment and then to campus. "I love bicycling," he said with a grin.

I soon learned why the large office Laird occupies is a chaos of papers on top of papers: Charles is a multitasking individual. In addition to being a professor of biology at the University of Washington, he coordinates the Fragile X Research Center for the Center on Human Development and Disability, one of three such research sites funded by the National Institutes of Health (NIH).

Next door to Laird's office is the "Laird Lab." This is where he and several co-investigators study cell and developmental biology, genetics and genome structure, and epigenetic diseases such as fragile X syndrome. Epigenetics, first defined by the biologist C.H. Waddington in 1942, is "the branch of biology that studies the causal interactions between genes and their products, which bring the phenotype into being."

Laird has authored or co-authored scores of scientific articles, and he is an expert in several areas of fragile X research, especially dealing with DNA methylation and mosaicism, and in developing methods and mathematical models to estimate rates of methylation. Fragile X is one of the disorders implicating inappropriate DNA methylation. Methylation is the adding of methyl groups (carbon and hydrogen) to DNA, which usually leads to turning off gene activity. Sometimes this is what's necessary in normal cells, but in fragile X syndrome the FMR1 gene becomes methylated inappropriately, switching off the gene's production of RNA. RNA produces the protein necessary for developing neural networks and proper brain functioning. Mosaicism describes methylation that occurs in some cells and not in others. The understanding of mosaicism is extremely important to scientific understanding of cell development and to clinical understanding of variation in fragile X and other disorders. "Mosaicism is one reason why variation among individuals with fragile X is so extraordinary, and can contribute to large IQ differences among siblings with fragile X," said Laird. "While the size of the CGG repeat strongly influences the probability of abnormal methylation, the degree of methylation mosaicism is the strongest predictor of phenotype."

As we began talking, what struck me initially was how genuine Charles was in wanting to know a little bit about me and my 15-year-old son, Noah, and Noah's point of view. "We tend to focus on the adult point of view," Laird said, "which is only one perspective. I'm interested in learning about the points of view of individuals like Noah who have fragile X. For example, how much does Noah understand about anxiety?"

"Well, he knows when he doesn't want to do something."

"Fragile X individuals seem to be extremely aware of what's going on around them," Laird said. "I wonder what questions would reveal Noah's understanding of anxiety?"

I said that it has taken me most of the last 15 years to learn how to just "be" with Noah without an agenda, to just hang out with him. As an example I talked about Noah's difficulties with transitions, moving from one activity to another, which is typical for Xers with the full mutation. "If I just relax and don't rush him," I said, "he will eventually move in the desired direction. But if I'm in a hurry or get anxious, then there usually are difficulties."

"What's your understanding of his conceptual life?" Laird continued. I responded by saying that Noah frequently surprises me with his level of understanding, even though he acts like a preschooler. I related how my wife and I frequently try to get at Noah's inner life by asking him to tell us a story.

"How's that going?" Laird asked. I responded by saying that Noah tells stories, often using TV or Disney characters, as a way to process his feelings about his emotions and the events of the day, especially if something has happened to upset him. He'll tell stories about what's important to him.

"It comes out in sentences?"

"Yes." I told Dr. Laird one of Noah's stories goes something like this:

Hercules

One day Hercules decided to walk to
the city. Knock....Knock....

"Hello."

"What's your name?"

"Hercules."

They shook hands and talked. They
went swimming. Hercules went home.

And here's another of Noah's stories:

The Tarantula

It was a dark and stormy night. There
was a tarantula. Knock....Knock....
Knock....

"What's that noise?"

It's the tarantula.

ROAR.

"What's wrong?"

Grumpy tarantula...

"Tarantula, go home."

"Great, great," said Charles, rocking forward, his longish salt-and-pepper hair bouncing.

I explained further that we've encouraged Noah's teachers to use storytelling with him to help him express himself. "The teacher and aides at school are now typing up some of these stories and sending them home to us, like the two I just shared with you."

Charles said that he thought it would be interesting and useful to capture Noah's words and phrases exactly as he says them. "The inexperienced person might gloss over the rough spots in the story, and probably not be 100 percent accurate in recording what the fragile X individual is trying to express. How much of the implicit humor, irony, and possible anxiety are originating from the recorder and how much from the fragile X individual?"

Talking about my son was a good segue into discussing the anthology—*X Stories*—I'm here to interview Charles for. I described a theme developing in the book: the dichotomy between putting our resources into relieving suffering in the future by finding a cure through research, or relieving suffering today by increasing community-based funding. So I asked, "By emphasizing research are we sending the message that Xers aren't okay the way they are?"

"I do think solving day-to-day problems is more important to fragile X families than where the research is going," said Charles, smiling, "and how fragile X families solve problems is the inspiring part of the story. As scientists we're hoping to make a positive difference in how things will work for children, adults, and families with fragile X.

"Scientists also solve problems to try to understand how things work. In biology, and especially in the study of human disease, there's a premium placed on the ability to solve problems. Fragile X is an unbelievably complex disease, and has some previously unknown aspects to it. For example, research into fragile X and FXTAS will contribute to a better overall understanding of biology."

After a pause to collect his thoughts, Charles continued with a sort of zeal: "The unusual inspiration is how amazingly well families do solving problems. In addition to the understanding of the underlying biology, it's important to discover how families solve problems related to fragile X and how they establish priorities to make things work." The FPG Child Development Institute at the University of North Carolina at Chapel Hill is actively investigating these issues.

Charles and I then began to discuss different advantages or disadvantages between living in a rural or urban environment. "In the early days of fragile X, in the 1960s and 70s, a lot of the cases were coming from rural areas, in both the United States and Australia," he said. "My understanding is that these fragile X adult males were working in agriculture, ranching, and farming, and were a functional part of the community. But the transition from rural to urban living didn't bring along with it a sense of belonging to a larger community for a variety of people. Our Center for Human Development and Disability has been involved with helping the disabled train for, and find, vocational opportunities in the greater Seattle area: for example, in restaurant training for those with Down syndrome."

Charles then asked if I knew Sam Israel, a young man in his 20s living in St. Louis. I asked if this might be the same Sam Israel I met at the 2004 FX Conference in Washington, DC. "That's the one," he said.

"Sam has spent most of those years since graduating from high school working at a restaurant. I understand he is cherished by his employer and co-workers. Sam apparently feels comfortable and useful there. It is important for people of all abilities to find something useful to contribute," Charles emphasized.

"I appreciate the opportunities that our earlier, more agrarian lifestyle may have offered fragile X individuals for working with others in the extended family and greater community," I said. "And the Americans with Disabilities Act has made the urban environment more accessible, as the Individuals with Disabilities Education Act (IDEA) has improved the integration of our classrooms. But today, in the state of Washington—and I'm sure this is true for many other states— excluding vocational training programs, or 'sheltered' workshops, there's still not one publicly funded place for the developmentally disabled over 21 years of age to go, where they can just hang out or recreate, if they can't perform satisfactorily a job-related task."

"I understand that," said Charles. "It's a huge concern. And I'm not surprised to hear you say it hasn't been addressed successfully. But I think we have to keep trying. We have to keep educating people to change that."

"There are two separate issues," Charles continued. "First, what does a full-time job mean? For a fragile X individual it might not mean 8 hours a day; it might mean 3 to 4 hours a day. Secondly, what are the living arrangements? I see them both as being important, but separable. We need to emphasize to the entrepreneurs in our communities the opportunities for them in employing fragile X individuals. It shouldn't be viewed solely as creating opportunities for the disabled. The opportunities flow both ways."

"How can those outside the disabled community learn to embrace it?" I asked.

Charles began by talking about Zach Weaver from Marysville, Washington, who was featured in two articles in the *Seattle Times* on October 26 and 27, 2005. Zach, a 14-year-old student, wanted to play football, the biggest sport at Cedarcrest School. After getting approval from the coaches to participate, Zach still needed help suiting up and making sure his pants and pads were positioned correctly. At first Zach's father did this for him, but soon Zach's peers started taking care of him. As *Seattle Times* reporter Brian Alexander writes in his article, "Marysville Team Welcomes 'Z-dog,'" during one game Zach appeared on the sidelines with his jersey on backward, but "his teammates helped him pull it off, turn it around and put it on the right way."

Zach couldn't participate in the contact aspect of the sport, but he did butt helmets and growl along with his teammates. And during fifth-quarter scrimmages after real games, the coaches from both teams allowed Zach to run for a touchdown. "Zach's relationship with his teammates is something nobody saw coming, and it's powerful enough to bring tears to the eyes of the coaches," writes Brian Alexander.

"The parents articulated the important message here," continued Charles, "which was 'Zach will most likely be in this community his whole life. Our goal as parents is to make sure he's a visible part of the community, so when he's an adult he will be known.' When Zach's peers on the football team are community leaders and business owners, they'll be more likely to hire someone like Zach."

Charles added, "You can see how these young people on the football team have known Zach, have fallen in love with him, just like the adults have; and they're going to be out there in the community themselves, hiring people, supervising people, or know where volunteer help might be available for Zach—or from Zach. After all, Zach can contribute as a volunteer, too. He can help out and socialize with others. Thus, the community issue is really an important one."

I'm reminded of my own son, Noah, when he was barred from the public library because he wasn't satisfied with just looking at the books and videos on the shelves; he wanted to go behind the counter to see the books and videos that were being checked back in, the ones that weren't available to him yet. One day the children's librarian even went so far as to come out of the building to physically block Noah and his caregiver from entering the library when he saw them coming down the steps. Even though I was so angry when I heard about this event I could hardly see straight, I had to turn it into a learning experience for everyone. Yes, Noah needed to learn proper boundaries, including where he was and was not permitted to go. But the library also needed to learn proper boundaries in dealing with the disabled. What could have escalated into a major confrontation with the library, my wife and I were able to transform—with the help of the ARC, an advocacy organization—into an opportunity to inform library staff about fragile X syndrome. In the long run, with a little bit of effort and accommodation, perceptions of Noah changed from a librarian's pest, a feared patron, into an accepted part of the library's family. Charles and I talked briefly about modeling in public these "best practices," if you will, for showing both our fragile X person and the public how to decrease anxiety, which is usually about just getting to know one another and becoming more comfortable in each other's presence.

Charles and I have talked several times about these questions of employment and community involvement. Charles emphasizes that because of what we now know about methylation mosaicism, we need to pay special attention to individual diversity and phenotype variability within the fragile X population. "The phenotype variability may be greater among fragile X individuals than in the typical population," said Charles. To underscore his point, he shared with me the findings of a major case study published by him and three other authors in 1997 in *Human Molecular Genetics*.

Within the general population, the average IQ is 100, and most individuals (68 percent) have IQ scores that fall between 85 and 115. This variation represents two standard deviations. Charles and his colleagues highlighted in their study the case of six sons, five of whom inherited the fragile X syndrome chromosome. The IQ scores among the fragile X brothers ranged from 62 to 120, thus spanning four standard deviations! Charles wanted me to understand that because of methylation mosaicism, there can be greater phenotypic variability among individuals with fragile X than is usually found in the normal population. He said, "It behooves us to look at each fragile

X person uniquely, and to pay special attention to individual variability, especially when integrating them into schools, communities, and places of employment."

Family Doctor: Interview With Roger Sharf, M.D.

Charles W. Luckmann is the co-editor of **X Stories**. *He has two children, Arielle (21), who is not a carrier; and Noah (15), who has the full fragile X mutation.*

Six thousand people call Roger Sharf their primary care physician. Over 100 of his patients have physical and/or cognitive disabilities. Since he began practicing in Washington State in 1992, he has had three patients with fragile X syndrome, a disability Sharf labels genetically inherited and cognitive.

I began my interview with Dr. Sharf by asking if labeling disabilities is helpful for treatment. "Doctors are labelers by nature," he said. "Part of understanding something is to pigeonhole it into narrower categories. I remember things better when I categorize. I'm inclined to define disability into what it is that is disabled, and then treat the patient accordingly."

A youthful forty-something, Sharf speaks slowly and earnestly. He rues the fact that in treating the disability he is not treating the patient as holistically as he wishes he could.

"My first exposure to fragile X was with two brothers, two years apart." Sharf said. "They came to my practice in the early 1990s with the fragile X diagnosis. I followed them for 6 years from ages 7 and 9 as they grew into adolescence. The scope of the difficulties they were experiencing got vastly more complicated as the boys got older."

"With respect to this particular family," Sharf continued, "I was impressed with the significant differences in how fragile X expressed itself between the two boys. The older brother was higher functioning than the younger. The younger in particular was more impaired cognitively; during puberty and early adolescence he was growing into a large man, and as a result of that his mother was challenged with how to deal with his cognition difficulties, in addition to the routine tribulations of dealing with adolescent emotions. It became a big deal for her for awhile."

"Did you prescribe medications as part of the treatment?" I asked.

"To my recollection, in consultation with the parents, the boys were not treated medicinally. The eldest was high enough functioning that the mother could talk to him, have reasonable conversations, and his behavior was not an issue. The younger brother, however, was more handicapped and became more and more a problem, but I can't remember using medications with either of them. At that time, in the late 1990s, the symptoms we targeted did not seem to warrant the use of medications. That seems a long time ago.

"They left my practice when the youngest was 13. It had reached a point when their physical and emotional outbursts became almost too much for the mother to handle. She was trying to deal with them, but there was little support she could muster outside of the family unit. This is typical for families with disabilities in the state of Washington. There is very little the state offers people in terms of taking care of the ill and disabled, especially those who had no choice in their illness or disability. I find this sad."

In doing some follow-up research to understand better where the state of Washington falls short in meeting the needs of the disabled, I discovered that there is not one day facility in the state of Washington that has a community focus and is open during the workweek for developmentally disabled adults over the age of 21 but still living at home, where their parents can send them for recreation and assistance when the parents are at work. According to Colleen Ersking, facilitator on Aging and Disability Services with the Washington State Department of Social and Health Services, all current programs for disabled adults "focus on finding that person a job," even though she admitted this was not possible for those with significant physical or cognitive disabilities.

I was interviewing Dr. Sharf in his home. He was on call and our discussion was interrupted temporarily by the telephone. When we resumed I asked him if he had any suggestions about working with fragile X individuals for family doctors and pediatricians just starting out in practice.

"One needs to have an interest in dealing with people you might have to think a little longer and harder about," he said. The gerontologist, the physician who takes care of older people, would have the same commitment—there are populations of people who need extra help. I would encourage any physician to lovingly take on that responsibility and not feel afraid to learn a little bit and prescribe a little bit."

"But there are barriers to physicians doing this. One is the obvious time constraint," Sharf continued. "You get paid no more to take care of a sicker person than a well person. As a family doctor developing a practice, it's easier to gravitate towards well people—who you have to do less for—because you will be paid the same amount. The relative rarity of some conditions will make it more challenging to develop the knowledge base to treat responsibly those individuals with less common conditions. The advent of the Internet makes it much easier for physicians to do research, should they choose to do that."

"Lots of physicians are in areas of medicine where they are thinkers as opposed to surgeons," Sharf said. "We live in a time period where if you're willing to do your own research and develop your thought process on what to do for an individual based on expert advice, you can do that responsibly without fear of doing something bad to somebody. For instance, it's very difficult if not impossible to get surgical expertise without surgical training, you have to be taught that hands-on. It's a vicarious learning process. But there are aspects in medicine that are thinking specialties, if you will, where I can learn what an expert does and I can adapt their principles to my practice as a foundation, which I do, and I would encourage other doctors to meet this challenge."

Before our interview started, Sharf had told me that during medical school he did both a 2-year residency in surgery and a separate, 2-year residency in family practice. That comparison helped him choose family practice as his specialty, so as a follow-up I asked him to further explore that dichotomy in his training.

"If you look at a surgeon it maybe takes 10 years for him to learn a particular technique with his hands and his mind. It's like learning to play the piano well, combining cognitive development with mechanical expertise. In general medicine we have procedures that we do, but a lot of what we do is purely cognitive, and prior to the Internet we needed to go into libraries to find the literature that would teach us what we needed to know, but often that literature would be years behind the most up-to-date technique or information. But with the Internet, information can often be only a month or two old."

"As the leading cause of mental retardation in boys," I said, "fragile X wasn't given that label until 1991, yet it's still very prevalent, one in every 249 women carry the premutation, but generally physicians don't seem very informed. At least that's the impression I get from talking with families who are trying to find pediatricians and family doctors who are knowledgeable about fragile X. The families I talk to are usually amazed that more doctors are not aware of the syndrome."

"I would have to agree," responded Sharf. "Prior to my involvement I would have been in the same category."

"What should parents be asking their doctor, both those families with a diagnosis and those without a diagnosis, but who have children experiencing developmental delays?" I asked

"In 2005, at least in the city of Bellingham, and I'd like to extrapolate that to cities across the country, at least those with a hospital, developmental delay should not be misdiagnosed. There's enough public awareness on the consumer side of health care, and certainly at the health care provider side, that a delayed diagnosis of developmental delay should not happen anymore. Early diagnosis of the causes of developmental delays, I would like to think, would be common knowledge among physicians dealing with children."

"What about older individuals with fragile X?"

"The phenotype of FX is quite variable, the indication has a large spectrum," Sharf said. "Moreover, we should be aware that for a young man or woman who is sociologically outside what I would call the conventional box, there is a high likelihood this person could be an undiagnosed person with fragile X, especially with women. This remains a very significant problem, especially with less affluent populations."

"For example," Sharf continued, "I have a young girl, 8 or 9 years old, who has just come into my practice who is obviously profoundly delayed, but she's been in foster care and bounced around from family to family within the state system. When she came to me she had never had a hearing test, nor vision test, nor had any blood workup ever been done on her. This is dismal, but common from my experience in the state of Washington.

"Thus, even those who have an established diagnosis of fragile X, unless they're born to a rich family and can buy the services they need to optimize the gifts a person with disabilities has, I have to report that the prospects are dismal, at least in the state of Washington where I have my experience—unless perhaps you're living in a city like Seattle, or another major city with a research medical hospital. Generally, across the United States, towns have not appropriated enough funding to help families cope with disabled loved ones. There is also a lack of funding in identifying those individuals in need, and in creating educational situations and social situations that can optimize what their lives have to offer."

"You think it's primarily a funding issue?"

"Yes. There are plenty of trained people who would love to be involved with this type of care; unfortunately, I don't see current administrations willing to invest enough dollars in their own people."

"Maybe we should spend a few moments just talking about the paradigm that we need to promote in order to change a system you call dismal," I said.

"I don't know this for a fact, but I would be willing to bet that in societies that are deemed more socialistic there is greater intensity of funding—in terms of research and outreach—for generating the help that individuals with disabilities can receive."

"There is currently a lot of advocacy work going on at the national level to secure funding for research on fragile X that will lead to a cure," I said. "There is also advocacy work to secure greater funding for educating the medical professions about fragile X, especially pediatricians. But from listening to you it appears that we need to advocate—perhaps even more strongly—for greater funding at the community level in order to help disabled individuals and their families get the assistance they need to optimize their quality of life."

"And what about respite care for the family?" Sharf interjected, heatedly. "This is probably the most important thing. Fragile X families need respite care regardless of income. And it is to be expected that people with disabilities will have medical problems, and that can be any kind of medical problem. Today fragile X is incurable. It's not progressive, but a diagnosis of fragile X establishes a pretty predictable path for the lives of most of these human beings. That is the same for Alzheimer's disease—incurable. Spinal cord injuries—incurable. Once diagnosed these individuals have a well-defined path to follow."

"Therefore, you have two major ways you can help these people," Sharf continued. "First, you can spend money researching the problem to see if you can figure out a cure so that you can prevent the disease from occurring in future generations, as well as a cure for the people already suffering from that disease. Secondly, money could be spent to reduce the degree of suffering for those who are currently experiencing the disease."

"Was the Americans with Disabilities Act of 1990 helpful in securing additional funding for these two areas you've outlined?" I asked.

"I commend America with the passing of the Americans with Disabilities Act of 1990, that is a start. But it's a small start in terms of trying to identify broadly people with disabilities and trying to solve some of the very simple, very basic means for these people, to get them integrated into society. If you really look at how much the ADA has actually done, you will realize that it hasn't really done very much, that it was actually a poor showing for a congressional action. For example, having wheelchair accessibility is important, but that is barely the tip of the iceberg."

"What you're indicating," I said, "is that to be fully integrated and respected as individuals in our communities and greater society demands increased awareness and funding for the family at the local level. But how do we raise the level of awareness that leads to the funding we need to assist families who are coping with disabilities such as fragile X?"

"It should start with public awareness as to the prevalence of how many Americans are living with significant disabilities. Fragile X, in and of itself, is relatively rare—the presentation of it in terms of the total number of Americans with disabilities is not very common. But there are many people who have family members with significant disabilities who live private lives—and can't live full lives—because our society is not yet ready to assign a higher degree of importance to their lived experience. Fragile X happens to be a less common disability, but as a cognitive disability, it is one of the more profound."

"The tragedy of fragile X," Sharf continued, "is that individuals with fragile X are highly functioning, or capable of high functioning, who have emotion, who have fear, who have all of the things that you and I have but with a significant paradigm shift, and so not giving people like this equity in terms of public funding and education and integration into society, I think, is cruel."

"Are there any other areas we should explore to help our readers understand the personal side of fragile X from a family doctor's point of view?" I asked.

"It ultimately comes down to love of another human being who is not typically within one's sphere or defined as a loved one. And the example I would give is if you had a person with fragile X who was disruptive to some degree in a busy waiting room, why should that cause office staff stress, or be perceived as a stressful situation for other patients and clients? What is so bad about somebody who acts outside of the conventional norm? Especially if the individual doing this is without intent of malice. There is a lot of prejudice right there that I see in my own waiting room. We as Americans do not typically embrace folks who are a little different. Generally we push to the periphery disabled individuals like those with fragile X syndrome.

"Moreover, it's amazing how many things we are capable of producing to make life more comfortable, but almost all of them have one thing in common, they have to make a profit for somebody else. It's time our society shifted their way of looking at things. Not that we have no examples of that, but we need to have more examples of just caring."

"And here we have an example of this when looking into the eyes of a person with fragile X," continued Sharf. "I would like to see our society not have to be bound by blood relations in order to be able to look into the eyes of people who are less fortunate than us, share that experience to some degree, and then appropriate enough caring to see if we can make their lives better. But caring is all about imagining the lived experience of someone else, in this case an individual with fragile X syndrome. Caring is realizing that living a shared experience is ultimately more rewarding."

Bride Of FXTAS

Terri A. Corcoran is an editor for **Mainstay**, *a publication for spousal caregivers, and a full-time caregiver for her husband, who has FXTAS.*

fragile X-associated tremor ataxia syndrome (FXTAS): the
degenerative neurological illness that struck my husband,
Vince, in 1999, shortly after our marriage. It was a second
marriage for us both; I was 48 and Vince was 64. FXTAS took
away practically all of what we thought our marriage would
be and totally overwhelmed our lives within 3 years, forcing
Vince into retirement and forcing me into the position of full-
time caregiver.

Falling: the first sign of Vince's FXTAS was that he fell down while
playing golf. He couldn't say why, nor could he ever say why
he fell as it happened more and more. Now we know he was
falling because FXTAS impairs balance. In the beginning
stages, Vince could get himself off the ground after he fell, but
as the falling incidences increased, he lost the ability to get up
by himself. This was a huge problem, as he was too heavy for

me to pick up; so, I had to find a neighbor or call the rescue squad to pick him up. Each time he fell, I modified how we did things so that he wouldn't fall again in the same way. But whenever I thought I had control of his falling, his body would find new ways to fall. Finally now, almost 7 years later, I have a much better grip on the situation, so a fall is very rare.

Five years: how long it took from Vince's first fall for us to get the correct diagnosis of FXTAS.

Five neurologists: the number of neurologists we consulted until Doc #5 finally got it! This quest for a diagnosis included several MRIs, EEGs, bone scans, nerve and muscle tests, and misdiagnoses such as atypical Parkinson's, multisystem atrophy, small strokes, and "the normal aging process"!

Full-time care: what Vince needs, because his balance and coordination are so impaired that he would fall if he tried to walk by himself. Because his cognitive functions are also greatly compromised, he doesn't understand that he shouldn't get up by himself, so he needs constant supervision.

Forgetfulness: a gross understatement for Vince's severely impaired short-term memory. Say three simple words and he will forget them in a minute. He only knows what day of the week it is if he makes a lucky guess. At times, he has forgotten who I am and he asks me where is his wife. But he can't tell me who he thinks I am when he forgets I'm his wife.

Fogginess: sometimes to the point that Vince will not respond to me at all even if I ask a simple question that only requires a yes or no answer, or a simple choice between two things.

Frustration: what I constantly feel because my husband of 6 1/2 years has had FXTAS practically since the beginning of our marriage. Vince is so disabled that we rarely go anywhere except to church, doctor appointments, and an occasional meal in a restaurant when I am feeling very energetic. Frustration because I cannot have a lucid conversation with the man I married who was a Ph.D. laser scientist, a brilliant man with interests from lasers and physics to theater, ballet, opera, sports, and politics. Frustration because the man who used to instantly devour every book that came into his hands now has a pile of books given to him as gifts in the past few years that have gone unread. Frustration because often I have to wait and wait and wait for him to take one step or put the toothbrush in his mouth and start brushing. Frustration because the man who used to teach me so many things is now totally dependent on me.

Freedom: what Vince and I have both lost because of FXTAS. Vince is totally dependent on others for all activities of daily living, and I cannot leave the house unless I get someone else to watch him. Ironically, the street we live on is called Freedom Lane.

Faith: what enables me to get out of bed every morning and persevere. I know that God has a reason for Vince's FXTAS, even if we don't understand it. I know that it has made me a much stronger person and has deepened my faith as I have reached out to God when no one else has been around to get me and Vince through a rough day. When I am feeling hopeless and desperate, especially at the times when Vince can't move or communicate with me, I know that God will help because He always has. Just when things get to where I don't think I can deal with FXTAS for one more day, things will let up a bit and I can go on. God has been truly faithful to me.

X chromosome: site of the runaway genetic sequence that causes FXTAS.

Xanadu: what living with FXTAS is not. Xanadu is a place of idyllic beauty. FXTAS is struggle and heartbreak.

219

Xanthippe: an ill-tempered woman—named for the shrewish wife of Socrates—which is what I often am because of my husband's FXTAS. It is very easy to achieve caregiver burnout.

Xeric: characterized by only a small amount of moisture, which is what I am not, as I often shed lots of tears from frustration and grief over what FXTAS is doing to my husband.

Toileting: let's just say that FXTAS involves a considerable amount of bladder and bowel incontinence, and leave the rest to the imagination of the reader!

Teeth: caring for Vince's teeth is one of my more arduous caregiver tasks. He is capable of brushing his teeth, but usually can't get motivated to begin. I'll put the toothpaste on the electric toothbrush, put the toothbrush in his hand, and he might sit for 15 minutes just staring at the mirror. I have read whole books waiting for him to get started. I have also pleaded with him gently and not so gently. I have begged, prayed, and cried. Finally, I found that what works the best is to bring his hand with the toothbrush up to his mouth with my hand—if he lets me. That helps focus his attention—sometimes. I'm still working on finding a solution to this problem.

Transport Chair: what I use when I take Vince out. It's too dangerous for him to try to walk outside. The transport chair is a lightweight wheelchair which folds up pretty easily. Vince can transfer from transport chair to car if I hold onto him and coach him along, but he gets easily distracted by anything going on around him and sometimes can't concentrate on moving the few steps that the transfer requires.

Talking: FXTAS has really impaired Vince's ability to form complete sentences or to ask or answer questions. If he wants something, he has trouble telling me what it is. His doctor has told me that I can't expect much emotion or understanding from him either, but this is not something I can simply shrug off or easily accept. Since communication is key to a marriage, we are really challenged by this. Luckily, Vince doesn't seem to get frustrated by this problem, but I do. I have learned to pray to God to help us communicate and to fill the empty spaces between Vince and me. Miraculously, this has brought me comfort. I try to find ways in which Vince and I *can* communicate rather than grieving over what we can't do. I get elated when we have a more or less normal conversation, which happens sometimes.

Ataxia: Vince's lack of coordination between mind and body. His legs are still strong and he is capable of walking, but his mind cannot tell his legs what to do. I get him to walk by telling him how to move his feet while I hold onto him. He can't take too many steps at once, because his mind gets confused with repetitions. He has to keep stopping, clear his mind, and then continue. But as grueling as the process can be, keeping Vince moving as much as he can is critical to avoid muscular atrophy, circulatory problems, and other medical complications. Aside from FXTAS, Vince has no other health issues, and I hope to keep it that way for as long as possible.

Attention Deficit: another difficult aspect of FXTAS. The man who had the patience and concentration to build a highly complex laser single-handedly now gets too distracted by a stray thread on the carpet to move his feet, or too distracted by a speck of lint on his clothing to answer a simple question.

Apathy: FXTAS has robbed Vince of practically all motivation to do anything or care about anything. This is a blessing for him, because he is content to be cared for by me and not have any responsibility, and he is in no physical discomfort. This is a nightmare for me because, well, my husband doesn't care about anything! He's not depressed, he's just apathetic. I, however, get depressed because I cannot be just apathetic.

Anger: what I have too often felt when overburdened by the responsibilities of an ill husband plus house repairs, finances, and every other aspect of life without my partner being able to help. When trying to straighten out financial problems caused by Vince's brain not working (before I knew it wasn't working!) and trying to fix up his house which was in total disrepair when we married (and which he promised to fix up, but FXTAS took away his organizational ability or desire to do so), I would lose my temper to the point of hysteria. I don't do that anymore, because when my blood pressure started to rise, I knew it was from—

Anxiety: and I recently went on an—

Antidepressant: which has helped tremendously, as much as I hate to take drugs.

Aide: I also recently hired a home health aide to help us 6 hours every day. Previously I had only a few afternoons a week of a respite caregiver so I could get out of the house. The every-day help is wonderful, but it's expensive, which is why I tried for so long to handle things on my own. But the rising blood pressure convinced me to spend the money, and I trust that when I need to go out and earn more, the Lord will help me find a job. For now, I am just trying to recover and to feel more human, as I have time every day to go out. I do my shopping, go to Mass several times a week, and see friends and my two daughters. I spend one afternoon a week with my adorable, darling, 1-year-old grandson who is the best medicine in the world! The aide showers and dresses Vince, and does exercises with him. He is actually doing a bit better now because he gets more exercise between the aide and myself than he did just with exhausted, burnt-out me.

Appreciation: what I crave from my husband for whom I give up all my physical, mental, emotional, and spiritual strength every day. His illness makes it hard for him to understand what I am going through, and he doesn't often express the appreciation I would love to have. Of course I understand that Vince has little control over this, but I'm far from being a totally unselfish saint, and the human side of me wants some kind of balance or give-and-take in this marriage. I tell him that someday when we're both in heaven (hopefully!), I want him to give me a *huge* bunch of roses. When Vince was well, he would sometimes buy me roses for no occasion and always on birthdays and anniversaries. But now I need them much more than I did then. As with all the other losses, though, I am learning to live without Vince's expressions of gratitude. I'm sure he appreciates me, and he *does* still say that he loves me. That helps a lot!

Acceptance: Vince's attitude toward his FXTAS, which is a wonderful attitude. He's satisfied that he has done many things in his life, including extensive travel, and is now in a peaceful place. I also am becoming more accepting, albeit very gradually, as God has put new people and new purposes in my life. This has enabled me to grow in ways that never would have happened had Vince and I spent the past few years just seeking enjoyment. I know God has plans for me, so I am trying to follow where He leads. My anger flares up much less frequently now, but I will still get times when the daily struggles overwhelm and exhaust me and all the negative emotions take over in my mind. How can watching one's husband deteriorate, knowing he will not improve short of divine intervention, not ever brings feelings of despondency?

Stuck: what sometimes happens to Vince. He gets "stuck" walking, where he stops and cannot move or respond to the verbal prompts I give him. So I sit him down, tell him to lift his knees so his feet get "unstuck" from the floor, and then usually he can get going again. I keep chairs and stools strategically placed all over the house, so there is always a seat within arm's reach for me to grab and place under Vince if he starts to fall. I also get "stuck" sometimes, when I just have to stop, sit down, and cry out my exhaustion and frustration.

Stamina: another thing that FXTAS has taken from Vince. He tires extremely easily and needs a lot of sleep to be able to function the little that he does.

Stair lifts: what we had to get on our two staircases to get Vince up and down steps. Other modifications to our house are a ramp out the back door, a handicapped shower with grab bars, a shower chair, and grab bars by the toilets.

Sanity: what I often feel I am losing because of Vince's FXTAS. It gets downright scary to be alone with someone with whom you can't communicate and sometimes forgets who you are. Once, Vince thought he was in a hotel in Phoenix, Arizona, and it took me over 2 hours to get his mind back home. I pleaded with him to "come back home" to me, and he finally did. Luckily, that hasn't happened since. My sanity is also severely tested by all the incontinence. Sometimes, it just all seems—

Surreal: it gets too crazy for my mind to accept as reality.

Support: it takes a village to deal with FXTAS. In addition to the home health aide, doctors, physical therapists, speech therapists, and nutritionists to keep my husband's condition from deteriorating, I need friends and family to keep *my* physical and mental condition from deteriorating. For mental and emotional support, I have joined the WellSpouse Association, a national organization of men and women who are caregivers for their chronically ill spouses. Through WellSpouse I have found a local support group, made friends who understand what I'm going through, and have lots of e-mail buddies with whom I can share woes and encouragement. Often I can even laugh with my fellow caregivers about the insanity of our lives.

Supernatural strength: what I have gained through my deepening relationship with God as I take the FXTAS journey. When I feel that I am just too small, just too weak, just too inadequate for this job God has placed me in, I pray for his mercy and help, and it has always gotten me through. I haven't run away yet, and I've even gotten my blood pressure down by learning to control the stress better. I rely on God to do what I think is impossible, because I know He can. Every day I have to go way beyond myself, and I have been amazed at what I've been able to do through God's grace. Physically, little me has been able to save Vince from near-falls and once in a great while even get him off the floor by myself. At night, I have to practically lift him into bed—he puts his knee up on the bed and then I lift him the rest of the way. As the FXTAS has worsened over the years, I have prayed to God for guidance and wisdom and have been able to figure out how to constantly keep modifying our lives to accommodate the illness. And emotionally, I have been amazed that I have more and more days when I feel okay, when I'm not an emotional wreck because much of my husband is no longer with me. Somehow, when I get very upset and pray and tell God exactly how I am feeling, I will gradually start to feel comforted. I can't explain how, I just do. That's how I know God is really there.

At this point, doctors have no cure for FXTAS, and they've offered very little advice on coping with it. I've mostly had to make up Vince's plan of treatment—basically, nutrition and exercise—on my own. The doctors can only assure me that the symptoms of Vince's FXTAS will get worse and worse. The only way I can mentally cope with daily life and with this wretched prognosis is to know that God is ultimately in charge, that He wants only the best things for me and Vince, and that

FXTAS must be His way of making us the people He wants us to be. It's not fun and it's certainly not a life I could ever have imagined even in my worst nightmares, but I see miracles almost every day as God leads me through this situation. I notice and appreciate every one of Vince's lucid thoughts and loving words much more than I ever would were he healthy. And now, in the middle of November when roses would normally not be in bloom, one huge, bright pink rose has opened on our rosebush. That's God smiling at us.

FXTAS Misdiagnosis: Interview With David Specter

Charles W. Luckmann is the co-editor of **X Stories**. *He has two children, Arielle (21), who is not a carrier; and Noah (15), who has the full fragile X mutation.*

Jerry Specter died in January 2004 at the age of 76. A few days before his death, after they read a published article about a newly discovered disease—fragile X-associated tremor ataxia syndrome (FXTAS)—his family had him tested for fragile X syndrome. Jerry tested positive. Jerry's daughter, Susan, suspected her father had FXTAS for two reasons. First, during the last 15 years of her father's life, medical professionals had trouble diagnosing the cause of his difficulties and decline. Second, Jerry's grandson, Noah Luckmann, is severely affected by fragile X, so Susan suspected her father might be a carrier, too, like her (see Noah's maternal family tree on page vi). Researchers had discovered that FXTAS affects 25 percent of males who have grandchildren with the full fragile X mutation.

Because Jerry suffered declining health in the last two decades of his life, because physicians misdiagnosed his symptoms, and because

FXTAS is mostly an unknown disease, I thought it would be useful to interview Jerry's youngest son, David, who was one of the primary caregivers for his father during the last years of his life. David lives a few blocks from his mother, Elaine, and saw her and his father almost every day in the years preceding Jerry's death. I know the Specters well; David has been my brother-in-law for 23 years. I conducted this interview over the Internet.

Question: In life Jerry was ambitious and successful. He went to law school at the University of Chicago and was involved in Chicago politics. But at the height of his career, he retired from his job and spent the next 19 years of his life mostly staying at home. At the time, what were some of your thoughts and feelings, and the thoughts and feelings of others in your circle of family and friends, concerning Jerry "dropping out"?

Answer: Jerry retired from his job at Acacia Mutual Life at age 57. When he first took his early retirement, I didn't feel that he was "dropping out," as he still remained active in Chicago community politics, such as the North River Commission. He also pursued starting his own company called Next Century, along with getting involved in investments in a local real estate company. Elaine and I both recall him being very energized during his early retirement years, and it wasn't until a few years later that he became more sedentary and disconnected from the outside world. Elaine's recollections of Jerry reflect a lot of manic, bipolar types of behavior during much of his early retirement.

Question: When did you first notice that Jerry had a tremor in his hands? Can you describe it?

Answer: I first noticed tremors when Jerry was in his early 70s. I noticed the tremors when we'd sit down together at dinner and he'd have trouble holding large plates and heavy dishes. At the time Elaine felt that the tremors were signs that Jerry had Parkinson's disease.

Question: When did you first notice that Jerry had ataxia, trouble keeping his balance? Can you describe the effect this had on Jerry and on those around him?

Answer: Elaine first noticed Jerry's ataxia and mobility problems when Jerry was in his mid-60s. We both remember him having trouble walking and balancing, which his doctor called "festination." It was difficult to see him suffer from these disorders, and we always had to assist him with walking, staying close by his side and often having to hold on to him to prevent a fall.

Question: Did Jerry suffer from depression, too, during the last years of his life? How significant do you think this was in affecting his quality of life?

Answer: Jerry's depression was extremely detrimental to his quality of life. During the last 5 to 6 years especially, he was very apathetic about so many things, including social and intellectual activity—two things he was addicted to during much of his life. During the last years of his life Jerry seemed most content staying home watching TV.

Question: Dr. Randi Hagerman has written that males suffering from FXTAS often have obsessive-compulsive disorder (OCD), and perhaps hostility and anxiety. Did you notice any of these events? Was there any sort of pattern you remember?

Answer: Regarding Jerry's possible OCD, he showed a lot of hostility and exhibited unusual behavior during his last 15 years. Elaine and I recall episodes where he would stand outside of his apartment building and yell at innocent bystanders for walking and driving through his building's driveway. He would also count cars from his apartment window. Elaine recalls specific incidents of hostility and inappropriate behavior towards her and others, such as verbally fighting with congregants at synagogue.

Question: When did the family seek professional help? What were the early diagnoses? How comfortable did you feel with these diagnoses?

Answer: The family first sought medical help when Jerry was in his mid-60s, although we met with most of the doctors later when Jerry was in his early 70s. Jerry's neurologists at Chicago's Northwestern Memorial Hospital never made an exact diagnosis. But they included hydrocephalus (abnormal fluid around the brain) and Lewy's disease (related to Parkinson's) as possibilities. His psychiatrist at Northwestern Memorial Hospital diagnosed Jerry as bipolar. We were always very troubled that a more precise diagnosis could not be made. Nobody ever seemed to know what was wrong.

Question: Jerry spent the last couple years of his life in a nursing home. Could you talk about some of the precipitating circumstances?

Answer: Towards the end of Jerry's life, his mobility became very limited and incontinence became a major issue. Memory loss—mostly short term—also became a serious issue during this period. After Jerry was hospitalized with colon cancer, it became very clear that Elaine would be unable to care for him at home. During his last years at home he was extremely uncooperative, apathetic, and difficult for Elaine to live with.

Question: What was life like for Jerry in the nursing home? What do you remember as most significant from these days?

Answer: Although it was extremely difficult and sad to see Jerry living in a nursing home, I realized that it was really the only alternative. Strangely, he seemed very content whenever I would visit him, and he never complained when I'd take him to his weekly chemo treatments. I still find this quite remarkable.

Question: Is there anything else you want to talk about related to Jerry's life or health?

Answer: My final thoughts for the interview are the recurring questions that I've had regarding Jerry's transformation from such a strong, energized, intellectual, and successful man into someone who seemed so sadly different towards the end of his life. I look forward to learning more about FXTAS, and I'm hopeful that my family will find peace and closure as we gain awareness and knowledge of Jerry's disease and his correct diagnosis.

Lessons In Life And Death:
A Physician's Perspective

Randi J. Hagerman is the Tsakopoulos-Vismara Professor of Pediatrics and medical director of the M.I.N.D. Institute at the University of California, Davis.

I am often asked why I spend so much of my time devoted to fragile X research and clinical work. There are many answers, including the exciting molecular advances that are related to what we see clinically, the benefits that are seen with treatment, and the appreciation that the families give us. Most importantly it is the connection with the patients themselves, and what they teach me.

The personalities of the boys affected by fragile X never cease to amaze me. I often think of the boy with fragile X who is clearly on the autism spectrum and yet he is able to connect in many ways with his peers and was voted homecoming king. I also remember the boy who graduated from high school and was the only student to receive a standing ovation when he received his diploma. Their sense of humor is much better than what you would expect from their cognitive testing, and their sensitivity and ability to judge people and emotions is remarkable. One mother told me that when she comes home from a bad day at work only her son with fragile X comes up to her and asks what went wrong that day. Her other kids without fragile X are often oblivious to her emotional state. Those with fragile X tell you right away what is on their mind if they are verbal, and they get into a pattern of interaction when they know you. Their eternal happiness is a joy to see in clinic. One young adult always yells in the hall when he sees me, "Hey girl, how are you doing?" His high-pitched greeting always brightens my day and the staff always laughs. We love him.

I am impressed by the parents and grandparents of kids with fragile X. Their strength in working with their children and in continuing to seek answers regarding treatment and better services is inspiring to me.

I want to tell the story of a mother who was also a grandmother and great-grandmother to kids with fragile X. I first met Amalia when I visited her house in California, not long after moving from Colorado to the M.I.N.D. Institute at UC Davis Medical Center. I was feeling a little down with the struggles of starting a new fragile X program and Louise Gane, the institute's genetics counselor, said, "Come on, we're going on a road trip to visit a family and you always love this!" We knew about this family because Amalia's granddaughter, Lorraine, works as a nurse at the M.I.N.D. clinic and told us all about her relatives who had fragile X.

Amalia was then about 80, tall and distinguished-looking, with a shock of white hair. She was articulate and kind and related the histories of her adult son and daughter with fragile X in great detail. She had prepared a wonderful meal for us and we had a delightful time talking. She did not mind at all that we examined everyone in the house, including her, and obtained blood samples on all. This was a warm and happy household that had done a tremendous amount to meet the needs of their children and grandchildren with fragile X.

Lorraine later told me her grandmother's story. She had grown up in Southern California in a Hispanic family and worked in social services all of her life. When she realized that she had two children with mental retardation who were not receiving appropriate services, she fought—along with other parents and professionals—to institute the Lanterman Act in California. This was a landmark law to establish regional centers to provide birth-to-death services for those with mental retardation, epilepsy, cerebral palsy, autism, and related disorders. Amalia was a fighter and was out picketing and protesting until the law was finally passed. In those days protesting was against her Hispanic upbringing and certainly not what her husband wanted, but she did it anyway for the needs of her children and others with developmental disabilities. She was one of the founders of the Eastern Los Angeles Regional Center and served as its board chair for many years. Later she was appointed by Governor Brown to serve on the Board of Developmental Disabilities in Sacramento. She worked throughout her life outside of the home, in addition to always meeting the needs of her family and children. Her last name was Guerrero, which means "warrior." She certainly was.

She participated in our Genotype-Phenotype study that involved neuropsychological testing. She was bright even in her 80s. She developed a mild tremor and ataxia in the later years of her life but that did not seem to slow her down. We were seeing far more severe tremor and ataxia problems in some older males with the premutation and had published on the fragile X-associated tremor ataxia syndrome (FXTAS) in men. At first I had not paid attention to Amalia's mild symptoms but after seeing an occasional female with FXTAS, we realized that Amalia's problems were probably on the spectrum of FXTAS.

At age 85 Amalia developed gastrointestinal problems that were evaluated at Kaiser, and they took her to surgery to rule out an obstruction. She had great difficulty recovering from this surgery and was dying in the Kaiser ICU. Lorraine called me because Amalia wanted her brain donated to our research. Our team headed to Kaiser. I was honored to be with the family and Amalia at the time of her death and to watch her last breath. As doctors we are privileged to be close to our patients in life and in death. But it is a psychological shift that I am still stunned by, to see the finality of death in your patient. To see on the gurney a patient who was so vibrant and full of life and love just a short time before, is unsettling even for a physician.

The secrets of life that Amalia taught us will be lifelong for me. After her death we carried out an autopsy at Kaiser—they would not perform it because of cost constraints, but they did give us space. Although Amalia died in the early evening, we were still working on the autopsy at 2:00 a.m.

Our autopsy team included Dr. Claudia Greco, a neuropathologist; her assistant, Jaz; Dr. Paul Hagerman, my husband, who is a molecular geneticist; Dr. Flora Tassone, the molecular geneticist who discovered elevated message in those with the premutation; Dr Sebastien Jacquemont, our genetics fellow; and Tristan Jardini, our research assistant. We all worked as a team under the tutelage of Claudia, who is a wonderful teacher. I had taken neuroanatomy in medical school but I did not know much at that time about individual patients or what was important pathology in each area of the brain. This woman I knew, and I knew disease, and what it could do to the brain. Overall, her brain looked good with very little atrophy, no obvious white-matter disease, and a nice-looking cerebellum. I breathed a sigh of relief. Amalia's brain looked better than some of the men that we had seen with dementia and FXTAS. Somehow, women with the premutation are relatively protected from FXTAS. This was good news for female carriers.

We worked hard that night, snap-freezing some samples from every part of the brain, then preserving other samples in gluteraldehyde. Jaz demonstrated his wonderful teaching abilities, gained through years of experience as an assistant in autopsy cases. He was finally going to medical school and he took pride in his knowledge and teaching abilities in anatomy. Claudia is a master teacher who gently and eloquently educates from years of academic knowledge and experience. We were a team united in this new and exciting endeavor. Everyone was learning and working so hard that we were overtired and giddy by the wee hours of the morning. It reminded me of the nights in residency when everyone was working together to save a patient. There is a rush like no other in life, and medicine is the only place that I have found this feeling. It is a combination of camaraderie, knowledge, exhaustion, helping others, and seeing something not seen in everyday life, all wrapped into one experience.

The neuropathology studies showed that Amalia had inclusions in her neurons and astrocytes that were identical to what we have seen in males with FXTAS. These inclusions have the fragile X messenger RNA inside of them, along with other critical proteins that when sequestered lead to neurological dysfunction. The good news is that they were less numerous than what we typically see in males.

We are still researching Amalia's samples. Her gift to us is priceless. We strive to make sure that this gift will continue to advance research to help find a cure for FXTAS and fragile X. This goal—like Amalia's gift—is also priceless and worthy of a lifetime of work with wonderful families. I am a lucky woman indeed.

Lessons In Life And Death:
A Granddaughter's Perspective

*Lorraine Ruiz, a nurse at the M.I.N.D. Institute at the
University of California, Davis, has five family members
affected by fragile X syndrome.*

I believe fate brought me and my family to Dr. Randi Hagerman
and her team of X-perts. I had relocated to Northern California from
Los Angeles in 1999 with my husband, Robert, and four children. One
year later my extended family joined me, including five family members
with fragile X. The cultural influence of our Mexican-American
heritage combined with the special bond that comes from growing up
in a family with special needs contributed to my family relocating. My
grandmother had lived in Los Angeles more than 80 years, but being
the courageous woman that she was, she had no hesitation in relocating
her family and planning for the one inevitable day when she would no
longer be able to care for them.

Grandma had three children. Both my uncle Albert, now age 63,
and my aunt Barbara, age 51, have the full fragile X mutation. My
mother, Molly, is a carrier. She gave birth to four children: my brother

Edward and me, and two children who are affected by fragile X. They are my brother, Henry John, and my sister, Elaine, who is the mother of Jillian, age 17, who is also affected by fragile X.

My grandmother devoted her life to ensuring that her children and others with special needs would receive appropriate services. Her plight began in the late 1940s when her son Albert wanted to attend catechism classes at the local Catholic church, and there was no program available for him. At the suggestion of the parish nun, Grandma gathered other parents in the community to begin fund-raising efforts towards this goal. This small, grassroots effort was the beginning of the special needs program in the Los Angeles Catholic Diocese. Grandma taught us that with faith all things were possible, and it was through this faith that her journey began. She continued to advocate for appropriate services throughout Albert and Barbara's lives, into their adulthood and their own aging process.

Our family has always been very close. We probably depended on one another more than most families because we had five family members with special needs. We are so close that our houses are actually situated next to one another. This might not work for some, but for us it just makes sense. I am a third-generation Mexican-American, with English being my primary language. However, there has never been any question as to my cultural heritage. We were raised to have pride in our heritage and to value and respect family and faith. We were taught to follow a strong work ethic and to balance this by enjoying life. I think that our Mexican Catholic upbringing has instilled in us a strong belief in fate or God's will—not in the negative sense, but rather faith that opportunities await us and we must be ready to embrace them. I also think our Catholic upbringing and strong sense of faith have helped our family in our acceptance of fragile X syndrome. We often travel as a tribe when visiting family or friends, and our family members have always been accepted with open arms.

My grandmother was a very independent and strong woman. She learned that trait from her mother and grandmother, who had relocated their family from Chihuahua, Mexico. In my eyes, there was nothing my grandmother couldn't do. She welcomed anyone into her home and made them feel like family. She could cook up the best Mexican or American meal in no time, and even ran her own restaurant when she was young. My grandfather was a musician and back in the 1930s and 1940s they owned a little restaurant in downtown Los Angles called Janitizio. My grandfather expanded the restaurant into a nightclub where a lot of the old Latin Jazz musicians performed. My grandmother ran the restaurant and the bar—in fact, she was one of the first women in California to get a liquor license. She always laughed about that because she didn't think it was anything to brag about. She had a fantastic sense of humor and could contort her face into the funniest shapes to prove a point or tell a story.

My grandmother often sewed with her mother, who worked as a seamstress to support her family as my grandmother was growing up. Grandma learned to sew without a pattern. She also crocheted beautiful afghans, which have become cherished family heirlooms. She could drive her kids across the country for family vacations, and she could change a tire. She was passionate about gardening and loved the feel of soil on her bare hands. She watered plants wherever she happened to be, even if it was a doctor's office.

She was independent and proud. When she became frail, even when she was recuperating from a broken hip, she practically refused to use a cane because she prided her independence. She would rather get assistance from a family member. She would also laugh at how aging is so humbling.

All these stories about my grandmother's passion for life and her spirit, however, don't begin to tell of the numerous organizations she was instrumental in forming. There are too many to list here! She was employed by and retired from the Eastern Los Angeles Department of Mental Health. By profession, she was a community worker and was able to advocate as a parent in her role. She was one of the parents who founded the Eastern Los Angeles Retarded Citizens Association. This became the Eastern Los Angeles Regional Center, one of California's first regional centers responsible for coordinating services to all developmentally disabled persons in California, from birth to death. This grassroots organization began in the 1960s and the regional centers were established in the early 1970s.

Grandma also was among the founders of a group called Fiesta Educativa, which in English means "Educational Fiesta"—a celebration of families coming together for the purpose of learning and advocating for their children. It is a support network for Spanish-speaking parents of children with disabilities. Fiesta Educativa holds annual conferences for the purpose of becoming educated in the area of disabilities.

My grandmother was also recognized by the State of California in 1976 as Mexican-American Woman of the Year for her contributions to the Latin community by improving services for the developmentally disabled.

I think that what makes my grandmother's accomplishments so remarkable is that she only had an 11th grade education. She grew up poor and had to drop out of high school to work when she was a young girl. Later she went on to obtain a degree based upon her life experience. She was very well read and often went to speak on behalf of families at the federal level. In retrospect, she often questioned herself and would say, "What nerve I had." But then she would say, "I just prayed and asked God to guide me and give me the words to help my children. Then any fears that I had would just disappear."

My grandmother was a woman with a brilliant mind and vision, who could speak with eloquent expression in both English and Spanish. She had a gift that drew people to her, and she used this gift to inspire others to organize. I observed these talents in my grandmother as I grew up, but they were all confirmed as I began to work as a nurse in the same field. I was often approached by people who told me how much they admired my grandmother, and how lucky I was to have her as my role model.

My mother followed in my grandmother's footsteps by working for the Eastern Los Angeles Regional Center as a service coordinator. She also served as a board member in the Los Angeles Chapter of the fragile X parent group. She has advocated for her children and continues to devote her life to her siblings and children in order to maintain their highest level of functioning.

I am a registered nurse, and I transferred from Los Angeles to the UC Davis Medical Center in Sacramento in 1999. One of our big concerns about relocating our extended family to Northern California was whether they would have access to good medical care. This is critical, as most parents and family members of people with special needs will agree. Randi Hagerman and her team relocated from Denver, Colorado, to the M.I.N.D. Institute at UC Davis in 2001. We felt that fate had brought Randi and her team to us, and maybe fate brought us to them. When my grandmother met Randi, her words were, "What a blessing."

To be honest, it was ironic that grandma felt so blessed by a researcher. She had not always had the best experience in this area, but she had hopes of finding answers to the puzzle and graciously participated in many research studies. You don't always receive immediate feedback from a research study. It is sometimes hard to wait for answers. She did believe in the end results, which often take many years, and was able to look beyond the need for immediate answers. Although she regarded her children as a blessing, she did imagine what their lives would have been like without fragile X.

My grandmother's final donation was when her brain was donated for research at the time of her death. It was a difficult decision for our family because there's a part of you that wonders, what if this contribution was made in vain. But we knew this was a gift that allowed my grandmother to keep giving of herself, even in death. Randi and her team were there with us with their warmth, their caring, and their brilliance. We encourage others to consider organ donation to find a cure for FXTAS and fragile X syndrome.

When I read Randi's description of my grandmother's passing, it brought back lots of memories of an incredible life that I wanted to share with others. My grandmother was such a beautiful woman, often compared in her younger days to Ava Gardner. The memory of her shocking white hair and her charismatic spirit lives on. The lessons learned from my grandmother are cherished and leave a legacy in our family that we are proud to pass down to our children and to our children's children.

My grandmother was proud of her life's accomplishments, but most of all she was proud of her children and her grandchildren. She said that she felt so blessed to be able to be with her family as she knew death was approaching. We felt so blessed to be with her as she breathed her last breath. She devoted her life to her family and children and Albert, her son, accepted her death so bravely. He was a role model for all of us as he calmly stated, "Okay, it's time for her to rest." Grandma hesitated a little before her death, and we reassured her that everything would be okay. She had prepared us her entire life for this inevitable day.

The Caregiver's View:
Interview With Gabi Quelch

*Paul S. Piper, a librarian at Western Washington University,
is co-editor of this book and of* **Father Nature**, *published by
University of Iowa Press.*

Gabi Quelch is a petite blond woman who radiates warmth and
trust. She was trained as a nurse in Germany. Without more training
she could not be licensed to work as a nurse in the United States, so
she began working as a caregiver, particularly for Alzheimer's patients.
A friend with a disabled child asked her to be a caregiver, and Gabi
subsequently signed up with the Washington State Department of
Health and Human Services so she could care for other children with
disabilities. She is currently a caregiver to Noah Luckmann, a boy of 15
with fragile X syndrome who lives in Bellingham, Washington. Gabi
has worked with Noah between 2 and 3 hours each day, 5 days a week,
for a year and a half.

Gabi says that an average day with Noah begins when Noah comes
home from school on the bus. Gabi greets him and takes him inside.
Depending on his mood, Noah either wants to eat or he wants to go out.
Gabi emphasizes that she thinks, talks, and accentuates the positive.

Noah doesn't like the word "No," so Gabi finds ways of maneuvering him around it. Instead of saying, "No, you can't go to Fred Meyer," she'll say, "Let's just eat something first," or, "I think it would be better if we went tomorrow." Gabi told me that fragile X children seem to have a special sense for people who take them the way they are and are not at all judgmental.

I asked Gabi if Noah ever talks about what happened in school, and she said only once. That exception involved a trip to McDonalds.

Gabi emphasizes that to do this type of work one has to be highly attuned to the moods of the person. It is important to be attentive to what Noah wants to do. Some days he wants to go to the park. Or they will go to the library or the video store, one of Noah's favorite activities.

Gabi plays with Noah, often by tickling him. I asked her if Noah likes to be touched, and she said not usually, but he seems to trust her. During their games she often changes her voice so she sounds like a variety of creatures. Sometimes they will play hide and seek, but Noah doesn't hide, and Gabi has to go back and find him.

I asked Gabi if Noah ever got upset with her. She said that he does, occasionally. But she always tries to enforce a safe space for herself that she wants Noah to respect. She told me about one incident where Noah hit her, then felt terribly guilty. He sat on the stairs and said over and over, "No hit Gabi, no hit Gabi." He doesn't like to lose control of himself like that. Gabi also told me about a recent episode where Noah was physically barred by staff from entering a public building. "He didn't understand why he couldn't go in and he got upset with me. I took it as a sign of trust, however. Noah knew he could get angry with me and I would still love him. And he had no other outlet for his anger."

Moods play a big role in the relationship Gabi has with Noah. When Noah is in a dark mood, Gabi will talk like a character in one of Noah's videos—Winnie the Pooh, for example. Noah has a special relationship with his videos and the characters in them, and Gabi uses this to make connections. Noah often interacts with the characters while he's watching the videos. He especially loves videos with music and bright colors. Gabi says she has tried to read to him a few times, but he doesn't like it. Nor does he like to listen to music outside of the videos. Noah often watches only certain parts of the videos. Gabi told me she is continually amazed that he is so adept at fast-forwarding or rewinding to locate the exact part of the video he wants. He's also extraordinarily talented at putting the videos back exactly where he got them. As a librarian, I especially respect this talent.

Gabi told me that Noah doesn't mind being with people he doesn't know very well. He had met her only once before she started caregiving. Then Gabi went on a trip and when she came back, the first time she worked with Noah she picked him up from the bus. He had not seen her since their first meeting, and she was overjoyed that he just went with her without any fuss.

I know I've had problems understanding Noah sometimes when he speaks, so I asked Gabi about that. She told me it was especially difficult for her to understand him at first, and that sometimes she still has to listen carefully. But now she knows many of the video characters he mimics and that helps. She can recognize that he is talking like one of the characters. Noah gets much of his language from videos, the words, expressions, and voices. He often wants Gabi to repeat what she says. Sometimes Noah picks up the phone and wants to talk to a video character. For example, if he pretends he's talking to Winnie the Pooh, Gabi will pick up the other line and pretend that she's Tigger. Gabi told me the simple elements that make up his world are extremely important to him, and he would not be comfortable if she didn't meet his needs. Being at home makes him the most comfortable.

Gabi told me that if she can make him smile it's enough gratification. She was responding to a question I had about what kind of goals she set for Noah.

She told me about a conference she attended once where someone told the audience that if you can make someone smile you've done your job. There are probably few people that Gabi couldn't make smile. "There is something very special and emotionally rewarding about this work," Gabi told me. "You don't get it from any other type of work." She feels that she and Noah are becoming friends. She sings to him and often he'll join in—not as harmony but as a call-and-response refrain. Gabi sings, "And I always will be with you," and Noah sings "With you!" She starts singing "You are my sunshine," and Noah sings, "My sunshine!"

Another way she makes him laugh is by pretending that she is going to "get" him. She'll say, "What are you going to do when I come for you, bad boy, bad boy" in a creepy voice and Noah melts with laughter.

I asked Gabi if she thought of herself as a teacher, if she had things she wanted to teach Noah. She said she's been teaching him right from left, and to recognize red lights when they are driving. She reaches for the conceptual projections that follow her actions. "What happens if I turn right here, Noah?" She told me that if she can make a game out of it, she can capture his attention. Noah seems to pick up a little bit. "It's very important that he learns to be polite, but it's also important that I am polite to him." She makes Noah clean up after his snack, put his shoes away, and say please when he asks for something.

One time at middle school the teacher took the class bowling. Gabi came to pick Noah up at the bowling alley. The teacher wouldn't let him go until he used a complete sentence to say he was leaving. Noah became very upset and threw a tantrum. Gabi felt the teacher wasn't at all flexible, that she pushed the request into a confrontation of wills. His new teacher—Noah is now in high school—is much more adept at playing by Noah's rules.

The first time Noah said her name, Gabi was thrilled. "I have no big expectations from Noah," she told me. "The small things are often thrilling, since I never know if they will happen or not." She gave me an example. "Every time I take Noah to Fred Meyer, when we walk by the flower display, I ask, 'Should we get a surprise for mommy? Should we get flowers for mommy?'" I know he likes to get surprises, and I'm hoping that someday he'll want to give his mother a surprise, too.

I asked Gabi what the key ingredients are for a job caretaking someone like Noah. She answered without hesitation that one has to have a lot of patience. Then she said softly, "It's not a job. It's in your heart." And Gabi has one of the largest hearts of anyone I've met in a long time.

And she told me that just the other day, Noah asked her to get some flowers for his mother!

A Trained Professional: Two Days With Rikki Resurrects An Expert

Steve Taylor lives in Oakdale, California, works as a therapist, and writes short stories, among other forms of literature.

I pushed Rikki down. She tried to reach into the cabinet again to get another tampon and I couldn't take it anymore. She landed on her ample butt and slid a couple of feet across the kitchen floor before her head snapped up and she looked me in the eye for the first time all weekend. I know it's impossible for someone like her to comprehend danger, but she seemed to read my face and knew it was safest to stay down. Rikki whimpered and started flicking her fingers. I stomped toward her and she flinched. I'm towering over this teenager with my fists clenched, chest heaving, wondering what the hell was happening to me. This was not part of the program.

There are only two reasons a human does anything: to get something or to get out of doing something else. This is the Behaviorist's credo. We Behaviorists try to break down everything a human does to these basic motivations and figure another way to get their needs met. No talk of self-esteem or Freudian voodoo. If you can speak, you pay a Shrink to lie on their couch. If you can't—you pay me.

Bring me a head-banging ten-year-old with severe mental retardation and I'd have it stopped within the month. I'd train some basic sign language and firmly tell him "NO!" when he went to hit himself and that would be the end of that. Rewards and punishments. Dog training delivered like a robot, that's what I do. I'm a real therapist and have the framed degrees on the wall to prove it. But no one believes me. I talk like a hick and certainly don't look the part: no beard, no glasses, and I will never wear sandals. There's no couch in my practice. Hell, I don't even have an office. Sometimes I make house calls. I put myself in *their* environment, working to change the structure of group homes and families to change the behavior of kids with real problems. I'm a Behavior Analyst. I'm an expert in changing behavior.

I'm three inches from Rikki and point to the living room, hissing: "Get in there." I'm too close for her to see me but she jumps up and walks quickly in the right direction. Rikki slaps the wall and breaks into a trot as the screaming winds up. The sound is primal and ascending. It speaks of complete loss and anguish a thirteen-year-old should not be able to feel. Rikki collapses on the couch and sucks in great, gasping breaths to push the volume higher. I grab her wrist and jerk her off the couch. I haul her to the bedroom and fling her inside. I punch the door closed and the house rattles. I will NOT give her another tampon.

"Intermittent-Explosive Personality Disorder" is your diagnosis if you throw extremely violent tantrums every few weeks for no particular reason. There's something called "Reactive-Attachment Disorder," which causes kids to be most vicious to those who love them most. Then there's "Oppositional-Defiant Disorder," which is self-explanatory. When their parents and schools and Shrinks can't handle them, I go to their homes and tell their folks what to do to fix it. Then I go home to my nice quiet condo.

Rikki has fragile X syndrome. A genetic problem that's like autism on steroids. Tunnel vision on the things they want, never handle change without aggression, and plenty of compulsions like closing doors and opening zippers. I'd been working with Rikki's mom and dad in weekly sessions for a couple of months. Here is what I told them to do: reward her with M&Ms when she waits patiently and send her to her room if she starts yelling. It's that simple. Her parents said she was doing a little better under my program.

Rikki's screams came through the door like a muffled jet fighter at takeoff. I knew from my clinical books that no human could keep that volume up for long, so I ignored it so as not to reinforce the behavior. Forty minutes later, it seemed she'd grown louder. When I agreed to take Rikki for the weekend, and into my nice quiet condo to boot, I didn't think about my neighbors. Several were clustered in my driveway, looking nervously toward my front window, shaking their heads. She had me. I opened the door to the kitchen cabinet and took out a tampon.

As she had gotten bigger over the past decade, Rikki's family found fewer and fewer people willing to babysit. She was about five feet tall now and 120 pounds of short-limbed, squat power in a coal-black pageboy. A dark, grimacing girl forever looking down. Her mom said the last sitter called and demanded they turn the car around only two blocks from home when Rikki started drinking from the toilet. That was five years ago. They hadn't had a break from Rikki since. I couldn't turn them down. So desperate was Rikki's family for a little breather they asked a single guy they've known for a couple of months to watch their teenage daughter for a weekend. Never mind that I'd never really spent twenty-four hours straight with one of my patients. I'm a trained professional.

They dropped Rikki off at my condominium on a crisp Saturday morning with a massive bag of food and a case of tampons. Fragile X kids were notoriously finicky about food, so I understood the sack but was scared of the other thing. I didn't know much about feminine hygiene, so I asked Rikki's mom if she was on her period or something. She smiled and told me, no, it was just something Rikki likes to have around and not to worry about it. I was happy to change the subject.

Rikki's parents were going to a nice hotel on a lake and gave me three pages of instructions and contact numbers. I told them not to worry. I was a pro.

I shall not forget the sight of that car's taillights fading in the distance. This was a seminal moment in my young life and career. I was truly alone with a person with a severe disability for whom I was responsible. I sighed and smiled down at Rikki as she sat cross-legged on the asphalt of the driveway, growling and flicking a toy plastic key. She reached up and took my hand. She selected one of my fingers and bent it downward so hard and fast I had to drop to my knees to keep it from breaking. I was able to get free a few minutes later and coaxed her inside the condo with a jar of Cheez Whiz.

I set her in front of the TV with the one video I knew she would watch—Jeopardy's Tournament of Champions from 1997—then returned to my office to write some more behavior programs. Seconds later, Rikki trotted in with the case of tampons, thrusting one in my hand and pointing to her crotch. Oh, no. Not this guy. I pushed it back at her and led her to the bathroom. She did not want to go in alone but came out minutes later making a high, chattering whine but apparently satisfied. Back to the TV. Back to my office.

It could not have been a full three minutes before she came in again, used tampon in one hand, the case under her arm. So this is why they sent a gross of tampons with her for a weekend. This is her compulsion. I decisively pulled the case from her and squeezed it high into a kitchen cabinet. She pinched my hips and lower back hard as I was reaching, but returned to her TV.

Over the next twelve hours, the above scene was repeated about every forty-eight seconds. The only variation was what Rikki did to us after I led her out of the kitchen. By turns, she bit me and herself and tore our shirts off. She kicked holes in two walls and vomited on my keyboard. Rikki snapped all fifty of her one-quarter-inch thick, hardened plastic keys like they were popsicle sticks. Around six o'clock she charged into my office and tore my master's degree off the wall and then stomped on it. The symbolism was over the top.

So I'm standing at the door of the guestroom, tampon in hand, ready to give her anything to stop the screaming and fighting. I'm mad and stupid and helpless. I'm an impotent bully. I feel a sudden kinship with every worker in every group home. This is what the families I work with feel like, maybe every day. I put the tampon in my pocket and pushed the door open.

Rikki jumped up from the floor and her screaming stopped like I'd pulled the plug on the world's loudest stereo. She obviously smelled victory and pulled her pants down for the reward she knew was hers. I calmly brought her out to the living room and pointed to the vacuum. I dramatically sprinkled tiny shreds of paper across the carpet. Rikki did not want to take the handle but stopped resisting when she saw the shreds disappearing under the vacuum and seemed to understand what I wanted. After she picked up the last piece, I turned the vacuum off and lobbed the tampon into the bathroom like a grenade, shutting the door after she ran inside.

Did I give in? Did I reinforce the screaming and violence? Even in my frustration and anger I was thinking like a behaviorist. I was proud of myself and my scheme until Rikki came into the office five minutes later, you-know-what in hand. This time I made her clear out the dishwasher, then she went to bed with a fresh one.

The next day was better, if you counted screaming and hitting me only once every hour as improvement. We communicated in a universal language. She'd cock her fist back and I'd point my finger like a pistol toward the bedroom. We both understood the contingency. Mutual deterrence, the politicians call it. My carpet got very clean and Rikki got new tampons about every forty-five minutes. By afternoon, she was approaching me, then turning on her heel and chuffing away because she knew she'd have to work for it. She even laughed a little a couple of times. I could not explain it, but Rikki didn't want to leave when her parents came to take her home. All our fighting and struggle, and her parents each had to take an arm to pull her into the car. Yet another thing I couldn't predict.

Clearly, I won. I worked through my frustration and even aggression to reach a level of understanding that has made me a better trainer, a better Behavior Analyst. Things are improved but not fixed. And that's good enough for right now.

I'm sure Rikki would say the same damn thing.

Artist: Ben Loeliger

Ben Loeliger, a junior in high school, is an honors student who plans to become an architect or engineer. He is a fragile X carrier and has a 12-year-old brother, Austin, with the full fragile X mutation.

This picture is about the connection within a fragile X family, and how they would interact, using an ecosystem as an analogy. The two tunnels represent my parents, and the water that flows through them give my brothers and me—the four trees—nourishment to live. The "M" above the large tunnel is for Mom, and the "C" above that tunnel is for "Carrier," as in fragile X carrier. The smaller tunnel is marked with a "D" for Dad. The stone steps represent the climb for a cure for fragile X, which is represented by the X in the tree trunk on the right, which is my full mutation brother's tree. I am the large tree, which is shaped like a "C," as I am a carrier also. There are several letters and words, which have meaning for me, hidden in the picture. Some of them can be found by using a mirror, or turning the picture upside down.

Siblings

Leaving The Body

Suzanne Roberts is an English instructor at Lake Tahoe Community College who has published poetry in many literary journals and anthologies.

I never had it as bad as Milo—
freckled across his broad nose, he
wore the same orange flannel, smelled
of old milk. Girls sang Dumbo,
boys pulled down his pants.
Mrs. Firestein made him sit
in the corner. Boys whispered,
elephant balls. They forgot about me.

Every recess, Mrs. Firestein made me
walk the straight chalk line she'd drawn
on the sun-blistered asphalt. She said,
We wouldn't have to do this
if you weren't such a lazy girl.

My right foot turned out—still does.
Daddy refused the operation—that's
my favorite story.
Mother found out about recess,
blamed it on the pliés in ballet class,
demanded Mrs. Firestein send me
back to play. In dodgeball, they aimed
for my face, called me Shazam.
I wished it were true.

Tuesdays, I went to something
called RSP. Karen Stauffacher led
the chant: Really Stupid People....
The grown-ups called Milo The Case
of the fragile X, which sounded
wholly better to me than my own case—
The Reversies. I put the m before the n
in animal, pronounced hamburger
in four syllables.

They made us look for words
in the big red dictionaries, got angry
when we couldn't find them, acted as if
everyone knows knife begins with a K.

They finally gave up, let us glue
model airplanes, cars, boats.
I glued the wing, counted,
one-one-thousand, two-one-thousand.
Milo turned round and round—an electron
orbiting a nucleus, earth circling yellow sun.
Like Francesca and Paolo, he rode
the flurry of his own wind.

The schoolyard emptied
into the gaping ribbon
of sky. I joined him.
We spun there together:
metal roof, elm, monkey bars....
Wooden airplanes flew
from outstretched hands.
The bell rang. I stopped,
stumbled across tilted blacktop.
Milo kept spinning in the whirl
of blue sky and heat, wind and glue.

The others ran toward us, pushed Milo
against the chain-linked fence.
He bounced with the ring of metal.
He threw up, found this way to leave
the body. They laughed and laughed,
so they didn't notice me there
with a one-winged airplane—
Shazam, the super girl, who flies away.

If I Close My Eyes, You Can't See Me

Debra Ann Borchett, a freelance writer living in the Pacific Northwest, has two brothers and a sister affected by fragile X syndrome.

My sister, Diane, had every reason in the world to be jealous of me. I was the eldest; she was the middle child. I had waist-length blond hair, a tiny nose, blue-green eyes; she had protruding ears, a slack jaw, glassy, honey-colored eyes. I had precocious charm; she had hysterical outbursts. I have a bachelor's degree; she has mental retardation.

I had no reason to be envious of my sister.

I remember Diane by her achievements. Potholders woven of multicolored nylon loops, à la Jackson Pollack. A tissue box cover: pink and white yarns drawn up, over, under the grid of plastic holes, empty spots grinning like a six-year-old missing a front tooth. A vase for a peach silk rose: a haystack of Popsicle sticks fixed together with purple glitter glue—her version of the Eiffel Tower.

Her face was like a Kewpie doll's, round as a cherry and as sweet. Her pale ivory skin was devoid of even the slightest blemish or fleck of impurity. Her eyes and shoulder-length waves were the color of honey. But lacking in her beauty was a steady signal of intelligence. There was not that spark that runs through a young girl's eyes that makes you want to run along with her and wish you could capture her, like a rare butterfly. Sometimes, when I looked into her eyes I felt as if might have been gazing into the eyes of a Guernsey: so filled with innocence and complete trust, with no other yearning or ambition than to be loved and taken care of. When Diane was calm, she seemed content wherever she was, for her body may have been with me, but her spirit was somewhere far away. At other times, she whirled about in a dervish of conflicting emotions.

When I was five I was "discovered" by a local owner of a children's clothing store. When Diane was five, she was discovered by her kindergarten teacher to have learning disabilities. Throughout our school days, Diane rode a small bus for the handicapped to a special school; I modeled at the Saturday afternoon country-club fashion shows.

Like all sisters, we were rivals. Every day when I arrived home from school, I raced to the refrigerator, tore off a few lettuce leaves, and fed them to my pet turtle, Tommy. When I found him covered in my frosted pink nail polish, my stomach twisted. No amount of prodding could get Tommy to poke his head out. He was dead.

Diane sat on the bed humming and combing her doll's hair.

"Diane, did you paint Tommy with my nail polish?"

She squeezed her eyes shut and pulled the quilt over her head. "You can't see me."

"What do you mean I can't see you? You're right there."

"Got my eyes closed. You can't see me."

Heat raced up my spine. But guilt squelched my anger. My stomach flip-flopped like it did on the first dip of a roller coaster. I picked up Tommy's terrarium with the plastic palm tree. I took him to the back yard. I placed him in his home and buried him. I did not cry. If Diane thought I couldn't see her because she had her eyes closed, how could she possibly understand that what she had done had killed my turtle? I couldn't be angry with a person who had mental retardation. Diane probably thought she was making Tommy pretty.

In the 1960s, doctors, scientists, researchers, Nobel Prize winners—despite their numerous attempts—could not identify injurious culprits, could not collect pertinent data, could not conduct conclusive tests, could not expose a mutant gene, could not produce concrete evidence on which to base their diagnosis: unknown cause of mental retardation.

In 1994, when I was forty, I learned that each of us had a fifty-percent chance of inheriting fragile X syndrome, the cause of Diane's disability. The fragile X gene was first mapped by a team that included Dr. David Nelson at Baylor University and Dr. Stephen Warren at Emory University. Our mother has one normal X chromosome, which she passed on to me; and another X, which she passed on to Diane. During the transition from my mother to Diane, the X chromosome mutated, for still unknown reasons, disabling her body to produce an essential protein. That protein facilitates synapses between brain cells and its absence caused her brain to not work properly. Rather than receiving a clear signal, Diane's brain was getting static and this resulted in her autistic behavior, her inability to count, her hard-won triumph of learning to tie her shoes at age ten.

Throughout our childhoods I defended Diane against bullies who called her "retard," against her own feelings of rejection when she was not invited to birthday parties, and against well-meaning *nice* people who spoke to her through me, as if she were deaf or not present. Along with the role of protector came a feeling of superiority—that no matter what I did or became, I would always be better than my sister who, as I was repeatedly reminded by my parents, was so less fortunate than I was.

Striving to retain superiority is a Sisyphean task. It does not allow opportunity for risk or for the chance to explore who you might be if you weren't so terrified of losing your footing and you actually levitate nine inches above the ground because you're so frightened of becoming retarded too, afraid that if you stop your brain from cogitating you'll lose its function and you'll be weaving potholders for the rest of your life.

By the age of eighteen, my looks awarded me a chance to leave my weather-battered upstate New York hometown and have a career as a professional model in New York City. Every Sunday at 5 p.m., I called Diane with news of the throbbing, filthy, cacophonous city that was now my home. I wished I could speak to my sister about my success. I was represented by Wilhelmina, one of the most prestigious modeling agencies in the world, not that she could comprehend this cachet. Diane not only did not read, but she also did not flip through *Vogue* or *Harper's Bazaar*. When she wasn't ripping up my magazines, she covered their pages with my Bonnie Bell frosted pink lipstick.

No matter how exciting my stories of celebrities met at Studio 54, Diane's response was: "Uh, huh. When you come home?" I changed the subject. I asked about her job clearing tables at the International House of Pancakes, her swimming in Special Olympics, the color of glitter glue she was using on her Popsicle-stick jewelry box.

I landed a national, network television commercial for Oil of Olay. Quite a coup as my projected earnings were $18,000—for one afternoon of work. And by "work" I mean having to sit still while a team of artists fusses over you, tells you you're beautiful, and asks if you are comfortable all the while heatstroke-inducing lights burn down upon you and you must try not to breathe, and make a conscious effort not to sweat, blink, or lick your lips because all that activity will disrupt the team's efforts toward perfection.

I sat in the studio dressing room and gazed into the mirror. The makeup artist fluttered about me, examining his blank canvas. With no makeup and straight, shoulder-length hair, I looked like I was seventeen, not twenty-five. My image transposed itself into Diane's. Her complexion had the smooth luster of alabaster. She had traipsed through puberty without a zit, blackhead, or worry about what boys thought of her. She had inherited our mother's aristocratic arch to her eyebrows, which I imitated by penciling over my blond feathers. Diane was taller, even when we were teenagers, although she was three years younger. If her eyes didn't look like she was so far away and lost, would she have been a model, too? If she hadn't been retarded, would she have joined me in New York?

Diane watched me now the same way she peeked out at me the night of my prom. She had sat on the bed we shared, her chin resting on her chest. Her limp, light brunette waves fell like a curtain hiding her cherubic face.

I struggled with the side zipper, slipped on my patent leather pumps, and cemented a stray curl with a burst of Aqua Net. I wanted to twirl around to see the effect of the taffeta lining; instead I sat on the bed next to Diane and put my arm around her shoulders. I tried to lift up her chin, but she grasped me in a hug and whimpered.

I held her while she sniffled. "You'll go to a prom someday, and I'll make a gown for you."

"Pretty."

"You'll be real pretty too." I wrapped the matching shawl around her and led her to the mirror.

I tipped up her chin. "See, you're very pretty."

She gazed at herself. I thought I saw a flash of light in her eyes, but it disappeared. Her eyes grew dull, without that fleeting spark. Her mouth spread into a smile causing saliva to drip down her chin. She stared at a place far beyond our reflections. Her eyes were like pools of honey inviting me to join her in a place where I never could go. I wanted to reach into them and snatch up the sister I knew was in there: the girl who would surprise me with a giggle, a perfectly timed hug, a brilliant sass-back to our mother.

My superiority did not rescue me from feeling helpless...futile.... alone. Not now, not even when she was right there right next to me breathing the same air I breathed.

Now the studio mirror in New York City revealed my adult self and the realization that I had never made a gown for Diane.

During our next Sunday afternoon telephone call, I did not mention my commercial. I had begun to realize that it would be cruel to speak of things that Diane would never experience. I never spoke about my marriage or husband, the photo shoots in the Caribbean, my divorce, or my dying career as I passed thirty. Superiority was an isolating business.

When she turned twenty-five, Diane moved into a group home. She was learning how to live more independently with limited supervision. She was also developing social skills to interact with people of both sexes who were not family members, people like her who also experienced intense emotional swings.

Overwhelmed by the loss of my attention-getting, income-producing, marriageable attractiveness, I withdrew into the cave of my superiority. Funny. I'd have thought that rank would reside at the principality of Monaco or along the Amalfi Coast, not a studio apartment on the edge of Hell's Kitchen. I had not spoken to my sister about my success. Now I could not talk to her about my failures— because I thought the complexity of those issues was beyond her ability to comprehend. And because I had the role of big sister to play. And superiors didn't stumble, much less fail.

I began to resent that I'd always played a protective role with Diane. I didn't recognize that I had myself to blame for having protected her from really knowing me—I had not given her the chance. Our regular Sunday phone calls petered out. I sent birthday and Christmas gifts, but I didn't call. I heard nothing from her.

After a few years of unacknowledged gifts and cards, a beige envelope sprinkled with a design of pansies arrived. An invitation to Diane's wedding. She was marrying a man who lived in her group home, who also was affected by mental retardation.

I knew I should be happy. Why wasn't I? I crumpled the paper. Why, in fact, was I angry?

I smashed the invitation into a clump. I flung it across the room.

She gets the government to pay her rent. I get to pay my rent. She gets Medicaid. I get to pay $12 a day for health insurance that covers abortion but not birth control. She gets to go to Hawaii. I get to go to the Jersey Shore. She gets to swim in the Special Olympics. I get to work my ass off. She gets blue ribbons for first place. I get old. She gets married. I get....

Oh, God. I'm jealous.

Jealous of my mentally retarded sister.

That's disgusting. That's selfish. I am a horrible, horrible, horrible person.

The same helplessness that pinched my heart and dragged it to my throat, that powerless feeling I'd felt my whole life for my sister, I now felt for myself.

I flopped onto my bed. I stroked a patch of the quilt. Diane and I had used scraps of the pink calico with red rosebuds to make matching dresses for our Troll dolls. She had been so proud that she had cut the tiny armholes and tied the ribbon around the doll's protruding belly all by herself. The fabric had faded but was soft as baby skin, soft as her cheek. Diane's eyes had flickered with joy for a few moments that day. I had hoped it would last. Every time I saw a spark, I thirsted for the whole being that I believed was my sister. But as always, her gaze had slipped away into never-never land. I was as alone then as I was now. She wasn't alone now. She was part of a couple.

I fell over onto my side and cried. "I'm not getting married."

I sat straight up.

Not only did I feel sorry for myself, I was no longer superior. What the hell role was I supposed to play now?

A laugh shook me.

A normal sister role. Everything I was feeling, was probably normal.

Normal.

This must be what normal sibling rivalry feels like.

Why had I thought that mental retardation would disable my sister from having a rewarding job, a marriage, a fulfilling life? Diane had been just as proud of her Special Olympic metals as I had been of my television commercials. She'd been as successful in her job at IHOP as I had been in mine, perhaps more so since she still had her career and mine had ended long ago.

I had tried to protect her; but that responsibility I had taken upon myself had distanced me from her and limited our love and our relationship. I exhaled. I felt lighter. A love I had never felt for her washed over me. I realized that acknowledging and accepting my jealousy and envy freed me to love Diane as my peer. Love her as my sister.

Her angelic face, partly hidden behind a wave of brunette hair, smiled at me from the silver frame next to my bed. I envisioned a princess-line gown in silk charmeuse with capped sleeves and a sweetheart neckline.

She would be a beautiful bride.

Growing Up Unique: An Only Sibling Of Fragile X-Affected Boys Discovers She's Normal

Angeline Schellenberg is a freelance journalist and inspirational speaker who lives in Winnipeg, Canada.

I missed the run-of-the-mill sibling issues that rub the edges off most children. While they did snap off my Barbie heads like any good baby brothers, Chad and Tim didn't insult my clothes, harass my boyfriends, or shoot down my political views. Hence, my acquisition of social survival skills—such as "staring at teenagers makes them want to kick you"—was a little stunted. I had unique sisterly challenges, such as explaining to the others boarding the school bus why Chad was running the other way or keeping my sleepovers out of earshot of the ranting coming from the basement bedroom.

If my parents noticed I was sinking socially, they hadn't the energy to intervene; it was spent adjusting their dreams. I overheard their conversations about how to maintain a friendship with a couple whose children were too uncomfortable to come to our home. I saw the tears they shed over other people's "picture perfect" Christmas letters: "Jimmy's excelling in lacrosse again this year and his science fair project on nuclear medicine won first prize." Unfortunately, they didn't have the support network then that they do now. Few of their old friends understood. So we kept to ourselves and I didn't socialize much with children outside my family either.

What I lacked in socialization, I made up for academically. At the wise old age of 14 I was convinced that I would become a reclusive genius, loved by no one, but admired by all for my brilliant musical and literary abilities. I felt a pressure, whether from within or without, to compensate for my brothers' lack of worldly success by my own overachievement. Then observers could take my grades, divide them by three children, and we'd equal an average family. (I realized later that 100 percent divided by 3 is 33 percent; but then math was never my strong subject.)

Looking back now I can appreciate the unique experiences I lived. There is nothing like the pride I felt screaming on the sidelines at Special Olympics track meets when my brothers won the relay. The knowledge that, after coming out on the bottom of so many spelling tests and Bible memory contests, there was finally something they could win at made it doubly sweet—although Tim would get more medals if he wasn't such a gentleman about letting his competitors merge into the center lane ahead of him!

And my eyes mist whenever I watch Chad lift a bar containing 470 pounds off the ground as if it was a broomstick. But that could be because my throat hurts from yelling, "Pull it up!" They always told me not to pick on him because one day he'd be bigger and stronger, but I never believed them, to my own detriment. He may be at a 6-year-old's reading level, but his memory works just fine.

Watching other children dare Chad to sit in a mud puddle during recess and running across the playground to stop him made me sensitive to injustice and marginalization. Since my social awkwardness had already rendered me an elementary school outcast, I had nothing to lose by defending him. I found out years later that there were other, more popular kids with mentally-challenged siblings that nobody knew about. I never considered keeping Chad and Tim a secret because I figured out early on that it was my classmates' prejudice, not my situation, which created the problem.

One day I came home from school crying. When my dad asked what was wrong, I told him some kids on the school bus called Chad a "retard." Dad got out a dictionary and pointed to the word "retard." It read, "To slow down." I think his point was that my classmates' word choice was loony because Chad never walked slowly. He was usually spotted in a cloud of dust! But when I think about that definition it reminds me of the ways Chad took life slow enough to appreciate things.

Like weeds. Sometimes he and I would sit by a ditch naming weeds and making up silly songs about them. Then we'd walk into a patch of the "Prickly Pricklers" pretending not to see them and stumble out melodramatically crying in pain. Or the times he shared his sense of loss—the dreams of what he would do if he were smarter, such as get married and make more money than his sister!

Tim, on the other hand, noticed keys. At the age when most toddlers are trying to jingle or ingest them, Tim was identifying entire rings of keys after being told only once what door each opened. During conversational lulls, Dad would ask for people's keys and get them to explain their uses. Then he'd hold the set out to Tim who'd easily say it back. The stranger's eyes would start to bulge, but we'd smirk, because we knew the best part was coming. Then Dad would shake the ring and cover up all but the very tips of each key with his fingers. People's jaws would drop as Tim told them the names of their keys by the shape of the teeth! Now he has his own set for his go-cart and dirt bike, as well as pockets stretched full of padlocks.

Learning to tie my shoes next to one who was learning not to hand-bite gave me a gift—the gift of comfort in the presence of a soul whose packaging is disfigured, or whose presentation is socially inappropriate. (Unfortunately, my comfort with inappropriateness is also reflected in my sense of humor!) Sitting with an elderly woman who can't speak, conversing with a gentleman scarred by burns, or pushing a child with cerebral palsy belted to a tricycle doesn't cause me the same discomfort that those who were not home-schooled by a fragile X sibling experience. I have enjoyed several part-time jobs with mentally challenged adults and physically disabled children. Getting paid for bowling, skating, and biking to the park is tough, but someone's got to do it.

When one of my college roommates accused me of failing to learn how to live with "normal" people I felt like saying, "What makes you think you're normal?" We all have limitations and quirks that need to be viewed through the lens of grace. Compassion and understanding, not IQ, should be the definition of "normal." It's not hard for me to feel for people who don't have it all together, because I didn't grow up with the Cleavers either.

But I have grown up. Thanks to my long-suffering roommates, friends, church community, and laid-back husband, I've come to accept who I am, which is neither a genius nor an outcast. I may not be typical, but I am "normal" in the best sense of the word: capable of giving and receiving love, forgiveness, and understanding. In fact, my lonely start makes me appreciate the rich friendships in my life even more.

When my parents need respite, I go home to watch my brothers, or more accurately, to watch *The Beverly Hillbillies* with my brothers. When I do, Chad reminds me about the rotten Easter egg that exploded 20 years ago and Tim reminds me to change my oil. And as we sit, quietly enjoying each other's company, my brothers teach me that people are not valuable because of the brilliant things they say or the awards they win, but because they *are*.

And that "reclusive genius" is an oxymoron.

"Hi, My Name Is Scott"

Carly Heyman has conducted several Sibling Workshops and is a contributor to **The Sibling Slam Book**. *This is an excerpt from* **My eXtra Special Brother**, *printed by the Fragile X Association of Georgia in 2003 and used here by permission.*

"Hi, my name is Scott."

It sounds like such a simple phrase, but for Scott it is not so easy. But why can't he just say it? Why can't Scott just look someone in the eye and introduce himself properly?

Introducing Scott to new friends has always been an interesting part of my life. I will tell you how I have handled my "Scott introductions" from the beginning to the end, and I hope it is helpful to you.

When I was about 7 years old, I did not even bother trying to give my friends a heads-up to the fact that my brother is unique. I always just went for it and said like any other kid, "Yeah, and this is my big brother, Scott." For most siblings that would be it: finished, done, no more questions. However, with Scott, it was a much bigger challenge.

I can clearly remember many times walking home from school with a new friend and finding Scott had been doing something odd, like talking to himself while playing basketball outside. I wouldn't think twice about this behavior, but my new friend would become uncomfortable, give my brother a funny look, and then turn to me for some answers.

I would feel responsible for my friend's feelings and would try to explain my brother's behavior. I didn't want to scare my friends away or have them think *I* was not normal just because my *brother* was not exactly normal.

After that awkward first impression, I would begin my typical speech: "Yeah, my brother is a little different; he has something called fragile X syndrome." Most often the responses would be, "Okay, but what does that mean?"

Even though I had grown up with him, I barely understood the term myself. How could I expect another 7-year-old to understand this complicated syndrome? I often tried to explain further by saying, "Fragile X is a type of mental impairment," and when this didn't work, I said that his brain worked differently, that he was born with this syndrome, and that because of it he acted a lot younger than he was.

There was always so much to explain, and at that age all I wanted to do was play. But I felt it was my responsibility to give my friends a reasonable answer they would understand.

Later, around age 11, I realized it was better to explain Scott's disability before people actually met him. Some friends knew other kids who had special needs, but most did not. It was always easier on me when a friend knew a little bit about people with special needs, but if they didn't that only meant I had to be more patient. Sometimes my friends would share a story about someone they knew with special needs, but usually the disorders they described were totally different from fragile X. Trust me, I've heard about some pretty extreme but unrelated conditions.

With my friends who were totally unfamiliar with mental impairments, I would have to start from the beginning. After my standard explanation, the questions would begin. Can he talk? Can he read? Can he walk? I don't know how many times I have answered the same questions, but as I get older, I am more patient and more willing to explain. The more open I am to sharing and answering these questions, the better the result. If I am enthusiastic and positive—and comfortable—when answering, my friends also become more comfortable. However, I will caution you that around middle school, kids tend to become more judgmental and less willing to accept different kinds of people. Trust yourself—and choose your friends wisely.

Although I've grown to enjoy introducing Scott to friends, there were many times when I wished he were normal so he could do it himself. Life would have been so much easier, but, hey: that's what makes it fun, right? It was difficult at times, but I never let it stop me from inviting friends over. Now at age 16, I find it a joy to introduce Scott to my friends. I start off with the typical: Scott…fragile X… special needs…mental impairment…etc. Fortunately, by the time they reach my age, most people are already familiar with the special needs vocabulary.

The rest of the conversation is usually determined by my friend's reaction. If they respond with "No problem," then we move on. However, if they start asking questions, then the "Scott introduction" speech continues: yes, he can talk; no, he cannot read; he has the academic capability of a third grader; no, he is not in a wheelchair; he is not physically impaired at all; and he looks like most other kids. Then I allow for a little pause to see if there are any more questions. Usually there are. What exactly makes him so different? I personally find this question the most difficult one to answer. I love him so much that sometimes I simply don't want to talk about his weaknesses. As a joke, I sometimes want to say, "Stick around, you'll see…!" but instead I explain that he does unexpected, weird things, cannot carry on a full conversation, and cannot express his feelings clearly.

That's usually enough, but with my more science-oriented friends, the questions continue. Where did this come from? I answer to the best of my ability and smile. I try to be patient and find the satisfaction in educating my friends about a subject they are unfamiliar with but in which *I* am an expert.

I find that my attitude towards Scott greatly influences the way my friends interact with him. I set the example. If I were embarrassed or ashamed of Scott, my new friend would immediately have a negative opinion of him. However, if I act like he is the coolest kid—which he is—my friends are more willing to develop their own silly jokes with him. It makes me feel good inside to see my brother socialize with my friends. But if friends, for whatever the reason, do not connect with Scott right away, that is also okay. I have found that the more time they spend in the Heyman household, the more they are going to warm up to Scott and want to be his friend.

When I finally complete my "Scott introductions," I *always* tell my friends how cool Scott really is. I say he is a great guy and an awesome and fun person to be around. I let them know how he likes playing repetitive little games with people and how it never gets old for him. I encourage them, for example, to create their own nicknames for Scott so he will love them forever. Some silly nicknames have developed over the years, including "Buster," "Uncle Scott," "Bubba," or even the greatest: "Meathead!" I usually end the introductions with these nicknames to finish up on a happy note.

Perfect Imperfection

Liz Seward is the sister of a boy with fragile X syndrome.

I cringe as my hubcaps grind into the curb, painfully screeching like a teenager forced to watch Barney, knowing the songs will be stuck in their head the rest of the day. Parking is harder than it looks. There are the curbs, and the other cars....and the curbs.

My car rests, bathed in fluorescent beams from the fixture above. I stop before turning the car completely off. I never like to leave the safety of my carriage with its noiselessness, its functioning air-conditioning system, and its grime-tinted windows. Someone should wash them. I don't know who. But someone.

Walking up the red brick pathway I spot a head peering through a window.

It's my brother, our family's surveillance system.

"Sissy!" reaches my ears as I ascend the two steps of the porch. Soon the dogs are barking: one a yip that could pierce a deaf person's eardrums and the other a low, guttural bark. I reach to turn the gold-painted knob but the door is already open.

"Hug Mom," Timmy sighs, handing me a picture of my boyfriend and me at the last formal school dance. "It's Nolan!" he exclaims.

A little white thing jumps up and down, scratching my exposed legs. I walk on, unfeeling, to the kitchen and find my mom for a hug. "Timmy, are you watching?" we call.

We untangle ourselves but Tim's back with an expensive glass vase, given to us by my aunt and uncle. "Flowers for Liz! Biiiiig hug!" he cheers, hugging himself by way of example.

My mom and I entwine again, as the white blur continues scratching and bouncing. "Annie! Quit it!" I yell at our little poodle, picking her up. I hold her like a mother burping a baby. She leans her head against my chest and sighs. Soon she's attempting to lick my face, getting closer and closer to invading my nostrils.

"Blech. Weirdo dog," I declare, setting her down again.

I make a run for my room but I'm not fast enough.

There's Timmy with my pseudo-wood plaque from water polo. "Hug Dad," he coerces. I trudge across the wooden living-room floors to the family room where my dad is on the computer checking his e-mail.

"Liz Seward. Best Offensive Player," he reads. "Well, you certainly are offensive!"

"Thanks Dad," I say, and, as an avid follower of the National Teenager Guidelines, I roll my eyes. "You know I practice just for you."

I turn to go. I have important things to do—like checking my e-mail for the forty-second time today and talking to people online that I don't really care about.

"Mooore. Mooore!" Timmy commands.

"How 'bout I hug Timmy?" I reach out and envelop him. He embraces one of my arms.

"No, Timmy. Give me a real hug."

"O.K.," he acquiesces, cooing, "Awwww."

Finally I head to my room for good, though Timmy calls after me with a manatee doll and PTA directory list, both very valid reasons for hugs. "No Tim, I have work to do," I shout back.

Entering my room, I pause and smile. Timmy's is not the kind of love that harasses you emotionally, burdening you with its expectations and problems. It's a love that keeps on giving. It can never be stopped. I know that no matter what kind of trivial "reality" I am heading back to, I have just experienced for one moment true, pure love.

Dear X-Men

*Katie McLane, currently a junior at the University of Mary
Washington, has a brother with fragile X syndrome.*

You've just blown up another science lab,
And you've escaped your doom until the next episode.
The only thing less real than those muscles
are the tears rolling down those cheeks.
You pose dynamically and I can't help but laugh,
as the world you are trying to save explodes
right behind your chiseled back.
And the blood and skin under that spandex,
and the heart that beats under those beefy pecs,
and the hands that bear those claws you hate
are because of a mistake.

Yeah, you complain about those genes,
and I don't mean the tight pair you're wearing.
And you probably don't know what a protein is,
only that it's in your breakfast cereal,
or what happens when a gene is methylated.

You won the genetic lottery, the Pick 5.
You got the lucky numbers, the million bucks.
You built yourself a mansion, got a jet,
some snazzy uniforms, and a fan base.
You don't know how lucky you are.

I grew up assuming that he would as well,
but he missed that magic number.
He lost that genetic lottery, he picked 6.
He will never have a mansion.
Kids like him aren't pilots.
His uniform is for a special school,
and he lived without making friends
for sixteen years, and never seemed lonely.
And it's because his genes are wrong, like yours,
but he's crippled in worse ways than angel wings.

You run around, you save the world,
and he can hardly save himself.
But he can sing The Messiah, and talk to Jesus
by kneeling at our kitchen counter.
He can make me laugh by talking
just like Edna from The Incredibles.
When we do the dishes, he can tell me
where all those weird spoons go,
and remind me to go to the bank.
And he never turns his back on explosions.

Sometimes, I want my brother to be you.
I want him to have laser eyes or super-strength,
or at least do fifth-grade math on his own.
I wish someone wanted to take him
to Canada and give him an adamantium skeleton,
because words, to him, are sticks and stones,

but broken bones mend faster than broken hearts.
And sometimes, I want you to see the world
through the eyes of my little brother,
who is more of an X-Man than you will ever be.

The Role of a Sister

Amy Bodnarik lives in Raleigh, North Carolina, where she works as a behavioral specialist for the Autism Society of North Carolina.

I can remember the first time it ever dawned on me that Doug was special and that I had a responsibility to help others understand him. I must have been about age 4 and my mother needed to drop us off at one of those walk-in daycare places. I knew in my mind that she must have a very good reason for doing this, but as I looked up at her while she was checking us in at the front office, I remember thinking, "This is not a good idea." A new place with new people was always a challenge but this time Mommy would not be there to make it all right.

I spent the time there hovering over Doug, making sure he didn't wander off, didn't get too close to the other kids, didn't get hurt on the equipment outside. It was exhausting. And just when we were starting to get comfortable with the little plot of playground area I had claimed as our own, a change occurred. It was now time to come in. I knew in my mind that there was a problem ahead.

Doug had difficulty with change. He didn't want to go in. He didn't want a snack. When I began to try to walk him inside, he pulled away and threw the biggest tantrum I'd ever seen.

A teacher came out and tried to pick him up to get him to stop, but that just made it worse. Another teacher came over and told me to go inside so that she could take care of the situation. Right then, I knew that I had to do something. Doug knew me. They were strangers. I knew what to do. They did not. So, just as I had seen my mom do many times before, I scooped him up and sat down on the ground.

As I began to rock him on my lap, I told the teachers, "He's my little brother and I know what to do." Within a few moments, Doug quieted down. A few minutes later, we went inside for a snack.

It was then that I completely understood that I was…Doug's sister. It was my responsibility to teach others about him. This was the defining role that I would play for many years to come.

Labels, Labels, and More Labels

Doug was one of the first few people in the U.S. to be identified as having fragile X syndrome. It seemed like no matter where we moved—and we moved a lot while my dad was in the Marine Corps—someone was interested in testing Doug, observing Doug, talking with my parents about Doug, et cetera.

It was a struggle for my parents to find the best educational placement for him since his identification seemed to be constantly changing. First, they said he had a learning disability. Then, he was classified as mentally retarded. And of course, at some point, he was placed in a class for kids with behavioral and emotional handicaps.

It wasn't until he was in his adolescent years that Doug was properly placed in special education programs with good special education teachers. It was this experience of seeing Doug bounced around from year to year with a multitude of teachers with varying skills and abilities themselves, that helped me to figure out what I would do with my life.

I eventually became a special education teacher. I wanted to make an impact in the lives of other children and families dealing with exceptionalities. I knew their struggles and understood their pain. But I also knew the fascinating and wonderful joy that these special people bring to our lives.

"Dougisms"

Doug seemed to hang on every word that we said. So many times, he would sit quietly and listen to conversations I had with my parents or friends. Often, I didn't know whether or not he was even paying attention. It wasn't until he was a teenager that I began to pick up on the fact that he was indeed listening to every word and watching every facial expression, usually out of the corner of his eye as he did not like to make direct eye contact with others. It was like he was studying us, trying to figure out the rules about communication and interaction.

Communication was difficult for Doug. Often, he didn't have the words to express his thoughts or feelings at the moment he needed to. This was frustrating to both him and the people around him. Often it led to "emotional fireworks," depending on his level of anxiety about the situation.

Sometimes when he was upset, he would rattle off the most creative expletives I've ever heard. Often, he would confuse some of the finer details of language, which made for hilarious "twists" of words. In our family these are known as "Dougisms."

For instance, my mother and I have always had a special connection. Often we will pick up the phone to call each other at exactly the same time. Sometimes, I will pick up the phone to dial her number and there she is, already on the other end. Every time that happened, my mom would say, "Well, we must have ESP!"

One day when I was away at college, Doug picked up the phone to call me. But before he could ask my mom for the numbers to dial, there I was, at the other end of the line, trying to call him at exactly the same moment. He was so surprised this had happened that he said to me, in a very excited tone, "Wow, Amy, we must have ESPN!"

Another example is from the time when my brother and I were growing up. Our dad had a little joke that he would make when we were out in public places and he was going to find the restroom. He would

say, "I'm going in. If I'm not back in fifteen minutes, send in the FBI."
Years later, my husband and I took Doug out to eat lunch at a restaurant
near our home. Towards the end of our meal, Doug excused himself to
go to the restroom, looked at me with a big smile and said, "If I'm not
back in fifteen minutes, send in the IRS!"

Body and Soul

In the winter of 1999, Doug was diagnosed with esophageal cancer.
This stunned our family since Doug did not fit the typical profile to
develop this disease. He was only twenty-eight, and a nonsmoker who
did not drink alcohol. But he had dealt with acid reflux problems for
years. Our family believes having fragile X syndrome was the origin of
his cancer.

We were blessed that my family lived only 30 minutes away
from Duke University Medical Center, one of the best cancer clinics
in the country. Doug underwent radical, reconstructive surgery.
Unfortunately, the cancer had spread to other organs in his body, as
well as his lymphatic system.

It was a long battle through chemotherapy, radiation treatments,
rehabilitation, and then a gradual loss of his functions that lasted about
16 months. But through it all, I have to say that Doug remained positive
and often spoke of the things he wanted to do when he got better.

We struggled to know how much to tell him about his prognosis.
He was like a child in a six-foot, three-inch body, and how do you tell
a child that he will not get better? Do you ever tell someone that? The
Lord does work miracles, but would a full recovery be part of his plan
for Doug?

As a family, we agonized over how much to say, what to say, and
when to say it. In the end, we decided to never tell Doug that he was
dying. But he knew. There came a day when I know that he knew. I
could see it in his eyes. He was getting tired and the fight was getting
harder.

Doug died on Sunday, May 28, 2000—the day before Memorial
Day. Although this was six years ago, I still have no words to describe

the tremendous loss and pain that I feel. I guess it is one of those things that you can never truly understand unless you've experienced it.

I have thanked God so many times for allowing me to witness the very moment that he left this place. I completely understand the difference now between the physical body and the spiritual soul. I saw this transformation take place. It was a profoundly sad moment, and yet I felt a shameful sense of relief that the struggle was over. His pain was gone.

I was left with a huge void as I realized for the first time ever that I would no longer have a role in his life. This was a role that I cherished. It was one that often helped me define who I was. Was I still a sister, even though he was gone? And why should someone with so many challenges to face on a daily basis have to die? Why was I left here? Survivor guilt had set in.

My parents and I all contributed to Doug's funeral service by speaking as part of a family tribute and eulogy. The church was packed as people came in droves to honor him. They even sat in folding chairs in the aisles to listen as we poured out our hearts and thanked Doug for all that he taught us.

Excerpt from Doug's Funeral Service: June 3, 2000

One of the things about Doug that I admire most was his unwillingness to feel sorry for himself despite the circumstances. He never questioned why he had to work harder to learn certain things or why he had to endure situations that others did not. He always accepted the challenges he faced without complaint, nor did he take for granted the small things in life that others tend to overlook.

I have a story that I want to share with you all. About 4 weeks ago, Doug and I were getting ready to go for a drive just to get out of the house for a while. I had been stressed that morning for many reasons. I was tired because I couldn't sleep the night before; I couldn't find a pair of pants that I thought I had packed; we needed to load up the wheelchair, pillows, medicines, go over emergency contact information, et cetera. It was evident that these little trips were getting harder for Doug to make.

I was so angry and sad that morning and I was having a hard time dealing with every little thing. On our way out the door, Doug put his arm around me for support and we walked out to the car together. As we walked, I found myself staring down at the ground, watching him shuffle his feet across the pavement and I began to think about how unfair the world is and what a bad day this was already.

Once we made it to the car, I looked up to tell Doug to get in. He was just standing there holding on to the car door and looking up at the trees and sky. With this big, almost magical smile across his face, he said to me, "It sure is a pretty day, isn't it, Amy?" And in that moment I realized that I have so much more to learn.

Doug was more aware of the beauty in his life than anyone I've ever known. He was always pointing these things out to me, but I just never took the time to really see what he was looking at until that day.

I miss my little brother so much and I just don't have the words to describe how it feels to be here without him, but I'm so thankful to him for all of the things that he taught me through the years.

Although I'm the one who grew up to go to college and learn to be an educator, Doug was the real teacher. It was his job to teach us all about how to meet life's challenges with courage and dignity and how to continue to live our lives appreciating all of the beauty in the world despite adversity.

He is and will always be a truly "exceptional" person and I am proud to have had him as my brother.

Artist: Amy DeBernardis

Amy DeBernardis was diagnosed with fragile X when she was 12 years old. She currently works at Family Outreach in Bozeman, Montana.

Contributors

Nancy Abrams, an award-winning author and photojournalist, is the mother of two sons with fragile X. She is a graduate of the Missouri School of Journalism and worked in West Virginia for 25 years. She currently lives in New Jersey.

Tracey Anderson, mom to Kellen (6) and Dorian (4), attended Colorado Mountain College and Pikes Peak Community College. She obtained her vocational credentialing through Colorado State University. Tracey worked at the Cheyenne Mountain Zoo for 11 years and is now the program and internship coordinator (and instructor) for the Zookeeping Technology Program at Pikes Peak Community College in Colorado Springs, where she lives with her two awesome boys.

Elizabeth Appell has published short stories in literary journals and e-zines. She is an award-winning playwright and screenwriter who recently won the Dorothy Daniels Honorary Writing Award. Her novel, Lessons from the Gypsy Camp, was published in July 2004 by Scribes Valley Publishing. Currently Elizabeth is working on a musical.

Barry Berg has been a writer and teacher for 40 years. He lives in Maplewood, New Jersey, with his wife, Susan Cohen—author of "A Fragile Strength"—and his son, Julian. Barry has been active in special education in his local school district and is currently co-president of the Special Education Parent-Teacher Organization for South Orange and Maplewood.

Amy Bodnarik lives in Raleigh, North Carolina, with her husband, Jeff, and son, Ryan Douglas. She currently works as a behavioral specialist for the Autism Society of North Carolina. Since her brother's death, Amy and her parents, Dean and Shari Pricer, have committed themselves to educating others about esophageal cancer through lectures and fundraisers. They have established an endowment fund in Doug's name to raise money for esophageal cancer research at Duke University Medical Center.

Debra Ann Borchett completed her career as a model and actress and is now a freelance writer living in the Pacific Northwest. Her essays have appeared in national publications, including The New York Times. She is currently working on a memoir about her two brothers and sister who are affected by fragile X syndrome.

Marcia L. Braden, Ph.D., is a licensed psychologist with a specialty in children and adolescents. She has written and published numerous articles related to education and behavior management strategies, techniques, and interventions. Respected for her work internationally, Dr. Braden has presented at many worldwide conferences and workshops about fragile X syndrome, autism, and other related disorders.

Sharon Carter has a medical degree from Cambridge University and currently practices in Washington State. Her visual art has appeared in Spindrift, Raven Chronicles, Disquieting Muses, Switched-on Gutenberg, and Soul of the Healer. Her digital prints have been shown at the Amy Burnett gallery in Bremerton, Washington, in conjunction with The Second Sunday reading series. Sharon is also an editor for Literary Salt, an online journal featuring poetry, fiction, nonfiction, art, and photography. She received a Hedgebrook writing residency in 2001.

Mary Jane Clark is the acclaimed author of nine best-selling suspense novels and is also a producer at CBS News in New York City. She is the mother of two. Her son David struggles with fragile X syndrome. Mary Jane is on the FRAXA Research Foundation advisory board and tries to raise awareness about fragile X awareness whenever and wherever she can.

Susan Cohen is a literary agent in New York City. She lives in Maplewood, New Jersey, with her son, Julian, and her husband, Barry Berg (author of "Plan B"). She now suspects that her late father, who carried the fragile X premutation, suffered from FXTAS.

Terri Corcoran lives in Falls Church, Virginia, and is a full-time caregiver for her husband, Vince. Before FXTAS disabled Vince, he and Terri worked together, organizing an annual international conference of laser scientists and publishing a monthly arts magazine for the Washington, DC, metro area. She is now on the editorial staff of Mainstay, a publication of the Well Spouse Association for spousal caregivers.

Amy DeBernardis was born on July 8, 1976, at Balboa Naval Hospital in San Diego, California. She attended ten schools from the time she was 2 1/2 until she graduated from high school in Bozeman, Montana, in 1997. Amy was diagnosed with fragile X syndrome when she was 12. She has taken courses in speech, sign language, psychology, and human development at Montana State University and currently works at Family Outreach, where she cleans equipment. Her second job as a global messenger for a local athletic club makes it possible for her to train for Montana Special Olympics in swimming, basketball, and track. Amy lives independently in her own apartment with her precious Labrador retriever, Beauty, has her driver's license, and enjoys playing the piano. She is an advocate for people with disabilities and was a presenter at the 2002 and 2004 Fragile X International Conferences.

Claire Dunsford is an associate dean in the College of Arts and Sciences at Boston College. A native of St. Louis, Missouri, she received her B.A. in English from St. Louis University and her Ph.D. in English from Boston University. She has been an adjunct lecturer at Harvard University and Boston College, teaching courses in writing, poetry, modern literature, narrative and interpretation, literature and censorship, and literature and illness. She is currently writing a book reflecting on her experience as the mother of a boy with fragile X syndrome, which is to be published by Beacon Press. A chapter from the book appeared in the Winter 2006 issue of The Kenyon Review. The eldest of five siblings, Clare and her three sisters are all carriers, and together they have four children with fragile X.

Tracey Franks is currently a graduate student specializing in print journalism at the Walter Cronkite School of Journalism and Mass Communication at Arizona State University. She is also president of the Fragile X Society of Arizona and the mother of a 6-year- old boy with fragile X and autism. Prior to returning to school, she worked in financial services for more than 15 years as an institutional stock trader.

Louise W. Gane, M.S., has been involved in the field of fragile X syndrome since 1984 and is the recipient of the National Fragile X Foundation's Jarrett Cole Clinical Services Award for 2004. She currently works at the M.I.N.D. Institute at UC Davis as a genetic associate. Louise is on a team working with Dr. Randi J. Hagerman on two research projects: Genotype-Phenotype Relations in Fragile X Families and Action Tremor and Dementia in Male Carriers of Fragile X. She is also part of the team working on another project, Neurological Phenotype in FMR1 Premutation Carriers. Louise is a member of the Genetic Counselor Core Group working on the Centers for Disease Control Collaborative Agreement for Cascade Testing and Genetic Counseling. She lectures nationally and internationally and is co-author of medical and scientific publications related to fragile X.

Elizabeth Griffin is the mother of Zachary, who is affected with fragile X. She is the author of the book Fragile X, Fragile Hope: Finding Joy in Parenting a Child with Special Needs, published in October 2004. In addition, she has published several magazine articles and made television appearances on the topic of fragile X syndrome.

Randi J. Hagerman, M.D., is the medical director of the M.I.N.D. Institute and Tsakopoulos-Vismara Professor of Pediatrics at the

University of California, Davis. She has carried out work with patients who have fragile X for many years, and authored or co-authored over 25 articles about fragile X in peer-reviewed journals.

Carly Heyman has conducted several Sibling Workshops and is a contributor to The Sibling Slam Book: What it's really like to have a brother or sister with special needs, edited by Don Meyer. When she was 16, Carly published the book, My eXtra Special Brother: How to Love, Understand, and Celebrate Your Sibling with Special Needs. She is currently a senior in the honors program at the University of Georgia, studying for her master's degree in occupational therapy. Carly greatly enjoys college life. In 2007 she plans to go backpacking in New Zealand.

Marie Horne lives in Raleigh, North Carolina, and is the mother of two adult children, one of whom has both fragile X and autism. She has a B.S. in social work from East Carolina University in Greenville, North Carolina, and has been an active advocate for her son and others with autism and/or fragile X. She served on the board of directors and the executive board of the Autism Society of North Carolina. She worked alongside other parents with the society to design and develop Creative Living, a unique day program for adults with autism. Creative Living serves as a model and attracts many visitors from around the country and the world. Marie enjoys reading, gardening, visiting with friends, and caring for her young grandson. She also works part time as a legislative assistant for the North Carolina General Assembly.

Nicola Jones was born in England but moved to Australia in 1968 at 16 months of age. She was accompanied by her parents, one set of grandparents, and an uncle, all on her mother's side. Her sister, Samantha, was born 6 years later and her brother, Christopher, arrived 2 years after that. Fragile X syndrome wasn't mentioned until Nicola's daughter, Maddie, was sent for testing in 2001. Results now show that Samantha, Christopher, and Maddie have the full fragile X mutation and that Nicola is a carrier.

Ben Loeliger is a 17-year-old honors junior in high school in West Chester, Pennsylvania, the oldest of four brothers. He is dyslexic and a fragile X carrier. His 12-year-old brother, Austin, has the full fragile X mutation. Ben has drawn and painted in surrealism art for more than ten years, with selected works chosen for local art shows. He plans to attend a four-year college and major in architecture or engineering. Ben has many other interests, including his Eagle Scout project, playing and composing classical piano, volunteering at the local hospital, and running cross-country on the high school team that currently holds the state championship.

Charles W. Luckmann has worked in archaeology, outdoor adventure education—Outward Bound—and academic publishing, as well as education at the secondary and postsecondary levels. Currently he teaches poetry, creative writing, literature, and ethnic studies at Skagit Valley College in Mount Vernon, Washington. He's continually inspired by his wife of 24 years, Susan Rachel Specter, who is a fragile X carrier, and by his two children (Arielle, 21, and Noah, 15).

Noah Douglas Luckmann did the cover art for this book, *Self Portrait.* He's a ninth grader in the Life Skills program at Sehome High School in Bellingham, Washington. He carries the full fragile X mutation. Noah enjoys visiting libraries, parks, and video stores. He is an avid videophile, collector, and storyteller. He was diagnosed with fragile X at the age of 18 months.

Katie McLane was born and raised in Farmville, Virginia. Her brother, Clint, is 3 years younger than she. He is her only sibling. Katie is 20 years old and a junior at the University of Mary Washington, where she majors in English.

Roberta Oberman is married and the mother of Eric, who is thirty, and Suzanne, who is twenty-five. She resides with her husband, Marty, and dog, Kody, in Florida during the winter season. In the summer she travels and spends time in Pennsylvania. She is an avid tennis player, enjoys a great novel, and loves to be outdoors. Her main focus has been raising awareness of fragile X and always being the best advocate her children could ever have.

Julie L. Peters is the mother of Colin, a 5-year-old with fragile X syndrome. She lives in Rolling Meadows, a suburb of Chicago. She is an assistant professor of history at the University of Illinois at Chicago.

Paul S. Piper is a librarian at Western Washington University, where he also teaches classes in information literacy, Internet literacy, and creative writing. He is a writer of nonfiction and fiction, and has published widely in small literary journals. He writes consistently on Internet issues for Information Today Company. He is co-editor of the book *Father Nature*, published by University of Iowa Press.

Suzanne Roberts works as an English instructor at Lake Tahoe Community College. She is pursuing her Ph.D. in literature and the environment at the University of Nevada-Reno. Her poetry has been published in many literary journals and anthologies, including The Adirondack Review, The Banyan Review, Branches Quarterly, Poetry Model, and Thorny Locust.

Lorraine Ruiz, R.N.C., is a psychiatric and mental health nurse, working at the M.I.N.D. Institute at UC Davis Medical Center in Sacramento, California. She serves patients and providers in the fragile X clinic, in pediatric neurology, and in clinics for child psychiatry and developmental pediatrics. She has five family members affected by fragile X syndrome, including her maternal aunt, maternal uncle, sister, brother, and niece. She lives in Cameron Park, California, with her husband, Robert, and their children—Jaclyn, Kathryn, Juliana, and Jonathan.

Angeline Schellenberg is a freelance journalist and inspirational speaker who holds a master's degree in Biblical studies. She lives in Winnipeg, Canada, with her husband, Tony, and their children: 4-year-old Gemma and 6-year-old Kieran.

Liz Seward is 18 years old. She plans to attend the University of California at Irvine and major in biological sciences/genetics. She enjoys playing water polo. Her brother Tim, now 15, is her biggest fan.

Paul Solotaroff is a freelance writer living in New York City. His work has appeared widely. He is the author of the book The House of Purple Hearts: Stories of Vietnam vets who find their way back.

Leonie Star, now a freelance writer who lives in Sydney, Australia, was principal of a major college for women for 6 years. In keeping with her wide interests, she has written books on a variety of subjects. She worked for the Fragile X Association of Australia for many years and was recently its president. She wrote and was responsible for the dissemination of 70,000 copies of a booklet explaining fragile X syndrome, which has been distributed to general practitioners, speech therapists, psychologists, schools, and special education teachers throughout Australia.

Judy Stringer and her husband, Jim, had two children of their own, Jess and Jea. Their blended family includes Jim's son, Jimmy, from a previous marriage. Jess was diagnosed with fragile X in 1986 at age nine. Jea tested negative. Judy is a carrier, as are two of her three sisters and two of her three brothers. Of nine nieces and nephews, only one—a girl—is a carrier. Judy and Jim knew Jess had mitrol valve prolapse and had tests done every six months. But the severity of the valve problem was not picked up and Jess died suddenly, while watching television. Judy, Jim, and the members of their family miss Jess every day.

Steve Taylor lives in Oakdale, California, with his wife, kids, and the world's greatest Labrador retriever. Steve works as a therapist to support his hunting and fishing habits.

Pat Tucker is the mother of six grown children, three of whom have fragile X. She serves as the president of the board for the Fragile X Society of Washington State. She is also a part-time instructor of religion at the University of Washington Institute of Religion.

Heather Vinduska was born and raised in Kansas. She graduated with honors from Wichita State University, and completed her master's degree in speech language pathology in 1993 at the same institution. She currently resides in Kansas where she now concentrates her time on being a stay-at-home mom and full-time advocate for her son, Vincent.

Rosanna Walther is an elementary school secretary and freelance writer. She has written many nonfiction pieces, including profiles, publicity announcements, and even a cooking column. Her grandson was recently diagnosed with fragile X.

Randy Weaver is the father of three. Amanda is 16 and a carrier of fragile X. Zach is 14 and has disabilities resulting from fragile X. Josh is 11 and is unaffected by fragile X—other than living with it daily in a family affected by it. Randy and his wife, Julie, have been married for 17 years and for 16 of those he has worked as an aerospace engineer. His writing experience includes Christmas letters and an occasional newsletter article. He is an avid golfer. His other hobbies include beer making and coaching youth sports.

Carolyn Ybarra, Ph.D., is the stepmother of a 19-year-old young man with fragile X syndrome, and she is active in the Northern California Fragile X Association. Carolyn coordinated the Education Project of the National Fragile X Foundation, resulting in the published Lesson Planning Guide for Students with Fragile X Syndrome. Dr. Ybarra is a professional genealogist and teacher of genealogy and creative writing. Her doctorate is from Stanford University in the field of cultural anthropology.

Resources

*Sources of help and additional information about
fragile X syndrome.*

Web sites

In this day of Internet accessibility, some of the most convenient,
authoritative, and comprehensive information about fragile X syndrome
can be found at the Web sites of the major fragile X organizations. We
have listed those here, along with their mission. These organizations
link to other state, national, and international fragile X organizations.

The National Fragile X Foundation at http://www.fragilex.org/ unites
the fragile X community to enrich lives through educational
and emotional support, promote public and professional
awareness, and advance research toward improved treatments
and a cure for fragile X.

CFXF, the Conquer Fragile X Foundation at http://www.
conquerfragilex.org/, provides information, fellowships, and
grant funds for research related to fragile X.

FRAXA, the Fragile X Research Foundation at http://www.fraxa.org/,
directly funds promising research to accelerate progress toward
effective treatments and ultimately find a cure for fragile X.
FRAXA also supports families affected by fragile X and works

to increase awareness of this important but virtually unknown disease.

M.I.N.D. Institute at http://www.ucdmc.ucdavis.edu/mindinstitute/, affiliated with the University of California at Davis, is an international, multidisciplinary research organization established to nurture hope as well as find better treatments and, ultimately, cures for neurodevelopmental disorders.

Books

The following list of books is by no means comprehensive. It is offered to provide a starting point for understanding fragile X. These books and many others can be purchased online from the National Fragile X Foundation and FRAXA Research Foundation.

Children with Fragile X Syndrome: A Parents' Guide, edited by Jayne Dixon Weber. Woodbine House, 2000.

Fragile: Handle With Care—More About fragile X syndrome (including Adolescents & Adults), by Marcia L. Braden. 2000 (Revised Edition).

Fragile X Syndrome: Diagnosis, Treatment, and Research, edited by Randi Jenssen Hagerman and Paul J. Hagerman. Johns Hopkins University Press, 2002.

Fragile X Syndrome: A Guide for Teachers, by Suzanne Saunders. David Fulton, 2000.

Fragile X Syndrome—A Handbook for Families and Professionals, by Brenda Finucane et al. 2002.

Lesson Planning Guide for Students with Fragile X Syndrome, by the Education Project Team of the National Fragile X Foundation. 2004.

Medication Guide for Fragile X Syndrome, by Michael Tranfaglia. 2000.

The Source® for Fragile X Syndrome, by Gail Harris-Schmidt and Dale Fast. 2004.